Down to Your Underwear, Please

Copyright 2013 treverbyn books
First Edition 2013

Cover designed by Amanda King
Printed by Palace Printers
ISBN: 978-0-9927886-0-5

For Beanie, Joshua and Ellie
'Los Reyes'

So many thanks to Mike Tate

Golden Rules of Osteopathy

A (very) tongue in cheek look at what osteopaths really think of themselves....

1. Osteopaths have more nerve endings in their fingers than ordinary people and so can feel more than mere mortals.
2. Any osteopath worth their salt can feel at least down to the level of a cell.
3. If you can palpate well enough you don't need a case history, examination, or any knowledge or thought.
4. You can get the patient better just by palpating them properly.
5. The better your palpation (as with eyesight, hearing and the sense of smell), the more intelligent, handsome and spiritually and morally superior you must be.
6. Research on palpation doesn't matter because osteopaths palpate on a higher plane which has nothing to do with mundane reality......

Well, it's important to retain a sense of humour in this dog eat dog world...

Contents

Introduction

My initial motivation for writing this book was to justify our existence in the world. Now, there's a task. Quite honestly, I occasionally find myself becoming a little fed up and worn down with the plethora of ill-conceived feedback from the public and medical profession and the rather confused picture they appear to have of us. I and many of my colleagues, can at times feel a tad insulted when we hear terms such as *'bone crunchers'* and *'placebo'* being applied to what we do. And so I hope to provide a bit more definition for those of you who are in the dark, and maybe answer a few of those burning questions.

There are still those in the wider medical profession (albeit fewer than there were a decade ago), who think that we are not to be trusted, that we pull bodies apart, eat babies' heads..... and, even worse in my view, that we discourage the use of modern medicine. None of this, of course, is a true reflection of us as a profession at all. But, I fear, we are not very good at disabusing people of these false impressions. My intention is to try and rectify that.

We are experts in our field of work, a field I hope to define in these pages. We are required to have an extensive knowledge of anatomy, physiology, neurology and orthopaedic medicine, and a wide appreciation of other *'ologies'* , such as pharmacology, as well as systemic disease and the immune system. We have to know how the body functions and how to recognise disease. As you read on, the reasons for this will hopefully become clear.

Dr. Benjamin Daniels, a GP using a pseudonym, describes most *'holistic therapies'* or *'alternative/complementary therapy'* (which osteopathy is deemed by most to be) as *'placebo'* in a recent book. In my opinion, he is rather ill-informed and has not been keeping up to date with the research. His main gripe against 'alternatives' is that we are *"ultimately private"*. *"Somebody"*, he says, *"is making money out of your illness"*. Oh Please.....

There are, of course, good and bad practitioners' world-wide, and, yes, some will undoubtedly encourage over-treatment. This is precisely why we are regulated and have complaints and investigations procedures.

I do not mean to write placebo off as unimportant. In fact, I hope in the following pages to stimulate your thinking on the phenomenon that placebo has become, and I cover the subject with considerable relish in chapter 15. It is a fascinating and provocative subject and I believe it is in the interest of all of us to appreciate its wider potential.

What 'Dr Daniels' and others of his ilk completely fail to acknowledge is that, besides easing the aches and pains of millions (yes, millions) of patients each year, we can also play a small part in patients' overall health, by crucial intervention when life may be at risk or when disease looms undiagnosed. Our training ensures that we possess the knowledge and expertise to recognise the human body's innate ability to trick its owner into thinking he or she has a musculoskeletal condition when they may in fact be suffering from something potentially more harmful, and requiring medical intervention.

Here's what I mean. A man in his late fifties, non-smoker, fit and seemingly healthy, presented with pain in his lumbar spine. It was not the result of a trauma and he had never had back pain before. So far, nothing exceptional. However, after further questioning, I learned he had recently been experiencing changes to his bladder habits, and, in particular, was having issues with the flow of urine and bladder emptying. This type of 'systemic' symptom is termed 'red flag' and we are required to relay this information to the patient's GP. On this occasion, some three or four weeks later, the patient was diagnosed with prostate cancer*. As I write, he is five years into his recovery.

This is not an uncommon occurrence – there are many more instances where our early diagnosis can help with more serious medical problems. Patients arriving with a back, neck or knee problem are often found, after 'sieving' down to a few possible diagnoses, to require further investigation in the hands of the NHS or a private medical practitioner.

Surely these patients would end up in the doctor's surgery anyway, you might think? Not necessarily. People often turn up on the osteopath's doorstep with the most unlikely of problems, before even considering visiting their GP. Consequently, we regularly find ourselves wading through a long list of possible causes, or 'differential diagnoses' in medical language. And some new patients seek us out because they have had a less than successful experience (through no fault of anyone in particular) at the

GP's surgery, either then or at some time in the past.

*Prostate cancer can present itself as lower back pain. Lots of true 'bio-mechanical' lower back pain is actually reproducible through movement and examination/assessment. Prostate cancer-related lower back pain does not behave like this and so can be a helpful in differentiating between it and musculoskeletal back pain.

We can be a 'last resort' for those who have exhausted all other avenues of intervention. That is an enormous responsibility. All the same, I continually find myself re-introducing to these patients the idea that their GP needs to know about their 'problem', and I frequently find myself relaying information between GP and patient.

As a profession we still have a lot to prove to a world that often views us with, at best a healthy scepticism, and sometimes, rather dismally, with deep suspicion.

To classify us as merely (not a word I use lightly here) 'alternative therapy' is not only unfair but also fails to recognise the extensive, not to say exhausting, training that we have undertaken.

In my view, osteopathy (manual therapy) is not an 'alternative' treatment. It is taught and practised to alleviate pain in the musculoskeletal frame and system (including the nervous system). There is nothing alternative about this. I do not meditate with my patients, I do not enquire as to their spiritualistic preference or meridian chakras (I've no idea what either of those are, by the way) and I don't believe that medicine, surgery or science are evil. Medicine often plays an integral part in musculoskeletal injury treatment – sometimes it is all that is needed.

I cannot comment on 'alternative therapy' *per se*, because I know so little about it – but from what I can surmise and through the brief encounters I have had with it, I believe it is world apart from the bio-mechanical world in which I live.

How do we osteopaths, chiropractors and physiotherapists go about changing this perception? I'm convinced we could start by joining forces under a common banner. Perhaps a collective name, such as 'manual therapists', might help us avoid continually confusing both the public and our medical counterparts about exactly why we find ourselves with three professions, chiropractic, osteopathy and physiotherapy that appear to do the same thing? I will use the term 'manual therapy' throughout this book, even though I *know* it will upset all three professions, but we should acknowledge that we share the same platforms and responsibilities and that our duty towards our patients is the same.

There are a few anomalies which separate chiropractic, osteopathy and physiotherapy, as you will see, but they are not important in the wider world.   Nor do our patients care - they simply want to get better. We continue to be guilty of confusing the public because we insist on promoting ourselves as 'different', when, in fact, all three disciplines are, in practice, more or less the same. There is not a huge amount that separates the three disciplines; our broad medical knowledge is excellent, and the same in each profession, while, once we've qualified, our varying techniques can be learned by each other anywhere in the country over a weekend (not always well, but that's 'unregulated' continued professional development (CPD) for you), or through post-graduate training. It's often only our attitudes and/or philosophies which differ. We all want our 'corner of the world', our 'autonomy'. This needs to change.

I came into the profession relatively late. Circumstances that I don't need to go into here delayed my higher education and I entered my 30s still wondering: *"What contribution do I want to make to the world?"* By then, my working life had already been fairly colourful. In my early 20s I was employed as project worker within an NHS-funded Drug Services Unit in

Berkshire, before spending a short period of time in the private sector with a well-known pharmaceutical trialling organization.

When I moved to my beloved West Country in 1998, I sought any job that was available, and was fortunate enough to be selected to 'trial run' the voluntary sector option of the New Deal Programme for the Job Centre throughout Cornwall, a project I continued with until the end of the third year of my degree. I had already dealt with lots of life's 'delicate' situations and knew that I wanted to continue in that vein of work. But, above all, I think I really wanted 'ownership' of a professional career in the health environs.

I'm fairly sure that, had certain events not panned out the way they did in my life, I probably would have trained to be a GP. I had always nurtured an interest in health and the human body, but I seriously doubted whether, at 30-plus, and with two children and a need to earn an income, I could commit to full time education. Very simple really; no hankering or grand desire, such as *'I went to see an osteopath and they were my saviour'* as others have experienced. (I did actually visit an osteopath a few years prior to my training and was not at all impressed) I just read the prospectus, which ticked all the boxes, and thought: *"Crikey, that sounds bloody hard"*. And it was.

There is a pecking order within the vast realms of medicine and I can't help feeling we feature somewhere near the bottom. An outpatient attending, let us say, a consultant rheumatologist's clinic, might mention that he or she is seeing/has seen an osteopath. The reaction and advice they receive from these 'professionals' can often be surprisingly scathing. This is unfair, and deeply concerning. I really don't want to sit in my little corner of the 'health' world, alone and isolated. We have a contribution to make to the world of medicine and everyone should be striving for a better understanding of one another and a more integrated approach to patient care.

My intention with this book is to throw some light on what we do and what we're up against for anyone who has ever visited an osteopath, thought of visiting one, or considered osteopathy as a career.

In the appendix you will find details of the large number of 'manual therapy techniques and intervention' research papers available from the Cochrane Library, which include others from smaller databases such as PUBmed and MEDline. These comprise systematic reviews (research papers with similar trialling techniques/interventions that are grouped together to form one large paper) and one or two meta-analysis papers (reviews of reviews). Again, I emphasize that this embraces physiotherapy, chiropractic and osteopathic research.

I have listed each paper separately and provided the reader with the author's conclusions – that is to say, whether the trial was successful or not and whether there were any further recommendations for re-trial. The trials listed represent 'un-cherry-picked' evidence as to the efficacy of manual therapy. I will throw in some anecdotal case histories throughout the chapters simply to help the reader understand the trial process from a manual therapy prospective.

Naturally, there is a humour in osteopathy, just as there is in midwifery, dentistry, teaching or any other walk of life, and I hope this comes through. Many of

Many of my patients have allowed me to 'indulge' in the telling of their unembellished stories, simply because they are hysterically funny and worth sharing, so a huge applause to the ladies and gents that have found themselves in peril due to misjudgement, animal adversity, poor luck or just plain dim-wittedness . Thankfully, humour finds its way into our clinics on a daily basis, and I've tried to share the funny moments along with the serious and the banal.

During my writing and research I have had some pinnacle moments - and I have made some rather disturbing discoveries. I'll even admit to moments of catharsis in one or two chapters. But, overall, I think of this book as a 'dissection' of the years I've put in and a glimpse at what we as a profession are up to in the 21st century.

In writing *'Down to Your Underwear, Please'*, I have come full circle in terms of my continued commitment to the profession and its future (there were times in its evolution that I gave in to doubts) but, really and truly, I write because I really like what I do for a living. There are very few days when I'm thinking: *"Roll on five o'clock (or, more usually, 8 or 9 o'clock)"*. I have the pleasure of meeting people from all races, cultures, ages and walks of life. They all have a story to tell....... and it's often me they tell it to.

I have a few people to thank and I list them here, in no particular order. Dr Ben Goldacre will probably be aghast if he ever reads this credit. However, when I first embarked upon the book, I went in all guns blazing, 'to defend the honour of osteopaths all over the world.......' (just kidding). His book, *'Bad Science'*, and his column in *'The Guardian'* inspired and urged me to try to present osteopathy in a truly balanced, non-biased ('ha ha', he'll chuckle) manner. Page 196 of *'Bad Science'* almost had me hanging up my clinic coat*, and I began to like less and less what I did for a living.

Being a perpetrator of genocide was not what I signed up for. However, it quickly became obvious to me that *all* 'alternatives'

---

*Dr. Goldacre, along with other colleagues, argues that Mattias Rath (who described himself as 'South Africa's leading AIDS dissident') was responsible, among others, for misleading the Western Cape of South African Government into believing that his vitamin supplements were a more effective treatment of AIDS than the drug AZT, which, as a result, left many sufferers without effective medication for a period of years and led to the early deaths of thousands. "Rath", he says, "is a dangerous alternative therapist". If mainstream medicine views osteopaths as alternative therapy, does this mean that we too are just as guilty of contributing to the mêlée of ill-founded information?

indeed *should* be answering to their critics just as the wider world 'critiques' the use of orthodox interventions by way of evidence based medicine, if they are ever to be taken seriously.

Inspirational, too, has been Caroline Stone. Her book, *'Science in the Art of Osteopathy'*, is a thorough exploration of the neurophysiology behind the practice of manual therapy techniques (in her case, osteopathy), and credits some of the leading influential bodies in the field. I was lucky enough to be a student of Caroline's in the early 2000s, when she took up the post of Principal at our college. She has seriously raised the credibility of our profession.

And finally, a delightful book that I take on holiday each year without fail, is *'Pain, the Science of Suffering'*, by Patrick Wall. Patrick provides the reader with a chewable 'mouthful', not only of the physiology of pain mechanisms, but also, and perhaps more importantly, of how pain can manifest psychologically, and some of its less understood phenomena, such as placebo.

Chapter 1 Sowing the Seeds

Definitions of osteopathy are many and varied (and often outrageously wide of the mark), but I fear that none of them totally describe the job I do – so it might be useful to begin with a summary of its origins and philosophy.

Andrew Taylor Still founded the first osteopathic school in Missouri in 1892, some years after the death of his father and three of his children from infectious diseases and having become dissatisfied with the medical practices of his time. It is claimed that he learned 'bone setting' with the indigenous peoples of America and that this influenced many of the techniques he developed. Faced with cynicism, he became an itinerant physician, talking to anyone who would listen about his new methods, which centred on treating the body by improving its own 'natural function'.

Initially, contemporary orthodox physicians were both sceptical and wary. Still's new science, whose adherents, or 'osteopaths', seemed to have a language all of their own, was difficult to comprehend and he was treated as something of a charlatan. The world at this time was full of unchecked 'miracle' treatments, including such wonders as *'Pink Pills for Pale People'*. Medicine as we know it was in its infancy but increasing populations were demanding better health care, and were prepared to 'try anything'.

But Still was clearly getting results. Word spread quickly, he was soon being sought out by patients from far and wide, and osteopathic schools began to open. Among his first group of students was a certain D.D. Palmer, who adapted Still's principles and theories to accommodate his own beliefs, and called it 'chiropractic'.

Then, twenty years or so after the birth of osteopathy and chiropractic, a nurse by the name of Marrianne Robinson, and three of her colleagues, established themselves as *'The Society of Trained Masseuses'*, which, in 1920, was awarded the Royal Charter - the *Chartered Society of Physiotherapists* was in embryo. Manual therapy was, therefore, all happening in a relatively short period of time.

Until the early 1950s, when Andrew Taylor Still's philosophy was developed into comprehensive 'tenets', deciphering his often elaborate osteopathic theories was no mean feat. However, his basic osteopathic principles are still taught today and underpin much of what we do and why we do it.

They are:
1. The body is a unit; the person is a unit of body, mind and spirit.
2. The body is capable of self-regulation, self-healing and health maintenance.
3. Structure and function are reciprocally interrelated.
4. Rational treatment is based upon an understanding of the above three.

Combine these initial notions with today's first class systemic knowledge of the body, and throw in a few handfuls of manual therapy techniques and examination processes, and you have the makings of a good osteopath.

Today Still's principles are hardly ground-breaking 'science', but they were innovative concepts in his time.

He understood, crucially, that physical symptoms should not be observed in isolation – that patients' minds and spiritual well-being should be considered too; that they are all inter-related. Poor human chemistry affects human physiology. He realised that, left to its own 'devices', the body generally jogs along quite happily (self-regulation). After all, it has been doing this every day for millennia, right down to the smallest of cells. And, finally, he believed that, if you undermine any part of the structure of the body, it will not be able to function in its entirety. This principle can be applied to just about anything on the planet, or indeed the universe - omit one ingredient from the mixing bowl and the results will alter.

Aside from these main principles, I wasn't too fussed about Mr Still, probably because he had the tendency to come across as a bit of a loon. To be fair, much of his written work was produced at a time when words and idioms had different interpretations and inferences, but I still chose to give his more 'questionable' beliefs and writings a wide berth. I don't want to detract from the foundations of osteopathy; but being noted for saying *"No two or more organs can work perfectly when one is crowding on another"*, leaves me scratching my head.

However, I did rather like another of his maxims, *'the rule of the artery is supreme'**; and *'arteries *rule ok!'* has been my computer screen saver for many years.......

Still was also a man of God and there is a strong religious influence in his work, which almost dismisses the 'science' within osteopathy. Science and religion make for uneasy bedfellows. Einstein himself ditched his when they began to be contradicted by the science books he was reading, while Galileo was called to Rome and charged with heresy for defending the Copernican doctrine that the earth was the centre of the universe and everything else moved around it.

He was to spend the rest of his life under house arrest - and was only exonerated by the Pope in 1990.)

The most compelling story of science versus religion, in my mind, is that of Charles Darwin, who showed that the evidence for evolution was, and is, clear; and yet we continue to venerate the relatively new concept of theology – a few thousand years compared with millennia of evolutionary data.

*One of Still's famous sayings was 'the rule of the artery is supreme'. Put simply, it is meant to imply that, if an artery is impeded, the rest of the body will not cope as well. In its infancy it was advanced; today it is elementary.

Perhaps we ought to re-define what we believe osteopathy to be in today's world and not rely on the description provided by one or two people, whose lives were shaped over a hundred years ago. If we consider ourselves to be a part of an 'evidence-based' system of medicine, we should not over-emphasize 'personal philosophies or religious entities'. Ironically, the 'philosophies' which underpin manual therapy disciplines may actually detract from its credibility.

Following America's lead, Britain set up its own colleges of osteopathy in the first half of the 20th century. Teaching methods and acumen were varied, but the principles were more or less the same. More and more manual therapy techniques were developed as the decades passed, adding to our already extensive knowledge of anatomy and physiology. The profession was not regulated but students were required to undertake a two year training programme to earn a D.O. (Diploma in Osteopathy).

Between the 1950s and '60s, 'proper' science began to enter the profession - we understood the importance of, among other factors, Newton's gravitational forces on the human body; Wolff's law (bone load adaptation); Irvin Korr and Co.'s 'facilitated segments'; and the 'pain gate' theory as explored by Patrick Wall *et al*. These new and important discoveries were accommodated in osteopathic teaching methods and, later, in university prospectuses.

However, our efficacy throughout this time continued to rest on anecdotal and word-of-mouth evidence, and, still bound up in philosophical and religious language that neither the general public nor the wider orthodox medical establishment could relate to, we were at risk of ostracizing ourselves as a profession. We talked of the presence of *'lesions'* as though they could be spread and caught, rather than manipulated. (*'Lesion'* in fact, referred to the tissues that are causing the symptoms, or "the hurting bit' of the patient, and was used widely among osteopaths until the late 20th century, when it was replaced by the word 'dysfunction' in most text books). People generally don't *like* the 'lesion' word.....

In 1993, the UK government brought in new legislation requiring both osteopaths and chiropractors to form, and register with, a governing body. And so, for the first time, we became 'regulated and standardised', either by the *General Osteopathic Council (GOsC)*, or by the *General Chiropractic Council (GCC)*. (Physiotherapy was, by this time, under the NHS umbrella and therefore already regulated).

You might have expected that this would be where any confusion as to what osteopathy is would be cleared up. Read on.

Definitions

The GOsC is the body that regulates my regulating of bodies, so to speak. I checked to see what its website has to say:

"Osteopathy is a system of diagnosis and treatment for a wide range of medical conditions. It works with the structure and function of the body, and is based on the principle that the well-being of an individual depends on the skeleton, muscles, ligaments and connective tissues functioning smoothly together.

"To an osteopath", the GOsC continues, *"for your body to work well, its structure must also work well. So osteopaths work to restore your body to a state of balance, where possible without the use of drugs or surgery. Osteopaths use touch, physical manipulation, stretching and*

massage to increase the mobility of joints, to relieve muscle tension, to enhance the blood and nerve supply to tissues, and to help your body's own healing mechanisms. They may also provide advice on posture and exercise to aid recovery, promote health and prevent symptoms recurring".

Not a bad description overall. However, two things merit comment. First, they talk of the body's "state of balance". But what does this mean? How do you gauge the body's "state of balance"? Second, it could mislead the reader into thinking that, as a profession, we are not in favour of drugs and surgery, which is simply not the case. In my opinion these messages tend to distance the boundaries between osteopaths and medicine, when they should be striving for integration.

What else does the GOsC do for its £600-ish per year fee? Well, it acts as the osteopath's executioner in the event of any 'mis or mal treatment' of patients, foul play or death.....to my knowledge this has not happened in the UK, but the potential is considered further in chapter 11.

Mmmm, oh yes. The GOsC regularly checks that I am practising safely by ensuring that I complete at least 30 hours of continued professional development (CPD) each year. This is aimed at assuring the public that we are a dedicated bunch of life-long learners. We document our training and analyse *why* we chose this particular course and how it has enhanced our professional practice. For example, I recently undertook a weekend course on vestibular rehabilitation (balance and hearing related problems). Why? Because, I treat enough patients with vestibular irregularities * to warrant learning how to differentially diagnose and then treat these types of disorders. Simple, really.

I have attended some rather excellent radiology CPD, run by the *Royal National Orthopaedic Hospital (RNOH),* and I have spent many a day observing relevant surgical procedures. I have also been welcomed by my local pain clinic, where I shadowed a senior doctor during a morning's work. I find this observational CPD much more informative, relevant and worthy than some of the CPD on offer to the manual therapy population.

*Patients presenting with vestibular rehabilitation requirements have symptoms of dizziness, motion sickness and visual disturbances, *inter alia*.

How does all of this 'assure' the public? I'm not sure the public are even remotely curious. However, in today's 'tick box' and,

more crucially, litigious society, most professions must be seen to be continuing to raise their standards of practice, to be adopting new and up-to-date measures, introducing IT packages, achieving scientific breakthroughs etc., etc. More importantly, the GOsC is there to monitor poor practising standards in the primary care world. A worthy cause, then.

Finally, it ensures that we have adequate public liability insurance in place; which means you, the public, are 'in safe hands' (the GOsC's motto...). The lesson here, folks, is, use the GOsC web-site and check that your osteopath is on the register.

Next we have the **British Osteopathic Association (BOA).** This is a professional membership organization, created to represent all osteopaths. It says:

"Osteopathy recognises the importance of the link between the structure of the human body and the way it functions. Osteopaths focus on the body's skeleton and joint function along

with the underlying muscles, soft tissue and internal organs.

"Osteopaths consider each person as an individual. Utilizing a highly developed sense of touch, they identify problem areas of the body. Using gentle" (my own patients might question the choice of this adjective!) *"stretching and mobilising techniques as well as manipulating joints, an osteopath works with the body to create the perfect conditions to facilitate the healing process"* ('recovery' would be better; 'healing process' sounds incredibly fluffy and unprofessional).

"Treatment usually consists of a combination of soft tissue releasing techniques and some specific adjustments affecting joints and soft tissues (muscles, tendons and ligaments). Advice can also be given on self-help treatments."

By this, I think I am correct in assuming, the BOA means lifestyle, posture, occupational and recreational advice.

Then, of course, there is **Wikipedia**, which offers:

"Outside of the United States, osteopathy has been considered a form of <u>complementary</u>

medicine, emphasizing a holistic approach and the skilled use of a range of manual and physical treatment interventions in the prevention and treatment of disease. In practice, this most commonly relates to musculoskeletal problems such as back and neck pain. Osteopathic principles teach that treatment of the musculoskeletal system (bones, muscles and joints) aids the recuperative powers of the body.

"In the UK, Australia and New Zealand, osteopaths have a 'physicianly' training, are **regulated primary healthcare professionals"** *(my highlighting) "and have never been subordinate to the medical opinion, diagnosing un-triaged patients and treating or referring them on as indicated. Some of these practitioners use the honorific 'Dr'. The distinction between American osteopathic physicians and manual therapy osteopaths may be lessening, with decreased communication between different countries and concurrent evolution of scope of practice* ''.

In fact, in the UK, unless your osteopath has completed a PhD in osteopathy, he or she may NOT use the title of Doctor or Physician. If they do, there is something very wrong happening.

Finally, this is what the **British Medical Association** (BMA) has to say, in its Guidance for Referral, published on 10 September 2009.

Referrals to 'complementary therapists'.

"This guidance has been produced in response to evidence of continuing interest amongst patients in the use of treatment modalities which are currently outside NHS healthcare provision but which are delivered by professionals who have statutory regulation in place. The evidence base for these services is growing.

Patients currently self refer, or are referred by their GP or other health professional and are increasingly likely to find these professionals as service providers within their Primary Care Trust (PCT). The majority of private health care providers now offer cover for these professional treatment services on condition that the patient is referred to the professional by their GP. Therefore, GPs may find numbers of patients requesting a referral for such treatment. The BMA's policy on referral emphasises the need for increased awareness amongst medical students and highlights the value of post graduate education for health care professionals. (This is almost certainly beginning to happen). Also emphasised is awareness that all practitioners providing treatment in the discrete disciplines of osteopathy and chiropractic have attained high levels of education and competence".

So, in the words of the BMA itself, we apparently know what we are doing?

"The aim of this guidance is to clarify the legal and ethical obligations of GPs in responding to requests for such treatment. The BMA welcomes greater use of the range of specialist skills within the health service, but needs to ensure potential legal implications related to referral to statutory regulated professionals are addressed.

"GPs are obliged under their contracts, or agreements with PCOs to refer patients to services available under the NHS whether through the usual routes or via newer provider service contracts. Referral to a statutory regulated professional on a private basis should

therefore not be considered a contractual requirement. However, in cases where a patient and their GP think treatment may benefit, a referral to a statutory regulated professional would fulfil the contractual responsibility. The GMC guidelines state that GPs should refer a patient 'to another practitioner when it is in the patient's best interests' (Good Medical Practice 2c). GPs may prefer to suggest that patients visit a particular type of practitioner if the patient is in agreement, without actually making a formal referral but can offer to recommend a suitable individual. In doing so, however, they must satisfy themselves that the individual is competent. GPs can generally be confident of an individual's competence by their continuing membership of the relevant regulatory body; however any specific concerns about a particular practitioner should not be ignored."

"A GP may not wish or feel able to advise a patient to consult a complementary therapist and therefore not wish to delegate or refer. In such cases, a GP is free to express their professional opinion; however they should make it clear that they have no objection to the patient independently consulting whoever they wish".

Changes to the Primary Care Trust (PCT) service, which may provide us with an opportunity to strengthen relationships with GP practices, are being debated among GPs, osteopaths, chiropractors and other non-NHS based health care organizations as I write. Depending upon where you live, there is a chance that manual therapy professions could be integrated into the NHS as a treatment option.

So … do any of these definitions of osteopathy cover it? Not really, not wholly. I don't want to discuss text book after text book, whether medical or osteopathic. After all, it took me many years to digest them and many more to put the masticated knowledge into practice, and, yes, I can hear you yawning already.

GOsC

The establishment of the GOsC divided qualified osteopaths. Many felt that it brought little benefit to the profession, citing, in particular, the cost involved in self-regulation and the lack of CPD provision, and they branched off in 1990, re-inventing themselves as 'osteomyologists'.

The GOsC was established to provide the public with information about the profession and to regulate all of us girls and boys who call ourselves osteopaths. The word 'osteopath' became a protected title - you had to be on the GOsC register to use it, or else face prosecution.

In the early 21st century, in collaboration with osteopathic schools, medical schools and universities, osteopathic training was developed to bachelor degree (and later MSc and PhD) level, and entered into the, until then, unknown world of 'evidence-based medicine' (EBM).

In 2003, along with the BOA and all the UK educational institutions teaching the subject, the *National Council for Osteopathic Research (NCOR)* was founded. NCOR's purpose is to develop osteopathic research and provide a database for its methods. However, osteopathic research remains woefully under-funded, is often restricted to small scale study groups and has difficulty in simulating treatments (medication is far more straightforward when it comes to comparative trialling). We have some way to go but, as I have said, we are still relative beginners when it comes to evidence based practice.

Towards the end of our osteopathic training, in the final year of our degree, we all get a taste of EBM, with submission of our dissertation signifying our entry into the voluminous world of randomised controlled trials and systematic reviews.......

Today, osteopathy is incredibly popular, not only in the UK, where there are over 4,500 practising osteopaths, but also in Australia, New Zealand, the USA and many European countries, in each of which, since the beginning of 2001, undergraduates have been trained to at least bachelor degree standard. There are similar numbers of chiropractors and as many, if not more physiotherapists. That's a lot of manual therapy going on.

However, we remain divided as to where we 'sit' within the orthodox medical world. Some of us, true to A T Still's philosophy, are vehemently opposed to joining the establishment, while others argue strongly for integration. My fear is that, if we don't communicate ourselves more clearly to our patients and the medical profession, we may be at risk of losing the 120 year battle to exist at all.

Chapter 2:   We All Stand Together

So, we have now established that there are a number of definitions of osteopathy. But on the day I started, I couldn't have given you one. As a first year student, I had little idea what osteopaths did, other than 'fixing backs', and I'm not sure I was entirely clear by the end of my fifth year.

How daunting, then, that, early in our first year as students, we were asked to write a treatise entitled, *'Myself as an Osteopath.'* I think even the most esteemed of my colleagues would agree that this must have been one of the more difficult assignments we were given.

It was rather like being asked to write *'The Rules of Parenting,'* having just given birth to your first child, or *'The Highway Code'* on completing your first driving lesson. None of us had any experience – how could we be expected to write anything sensible? I've no idea what I wrote and can honestly say that I never read mine again (although I'm convinced now that that was the purpose – that we should re-read it years later). By the time we were asked to repeat the exercise as fifth year students, I was much more confident about actually *becoming* an osteopath, and a vague idea was developing in my mind as to what contribution to the profession I might make - although I never saw this book coming.....

On turning 30, I had been coming to the conclusion that, somewhere in my head, there lurked a brain. I realised that I had rarely ever really pushed myself, even though my job choices had always been mentally demanding and required 'good people skills', as well as the ability to construe new and often complicated public and social health legislation. I had drifted in and out of a few 'business type' courses, was trained in drugs counselling and had gained a few other 'useful NVQs', but when I looked at my cv, I lamented its apparent shortcomings.

My children were by now both mostly settled and happy at school and I felt the time was right to take on a new challenge. Although I had never really been encouraged academically as a child, I had nursed, so to speak, an interest in medical matters and human anatomy for as long as I could remember. I tested my aptitude for learning just as I turned 30. The timing was right and ambition had found me, it seems. I thought a good start would be to aim at an A Level and I chose an 'AS' Level, Biology at Truro

College. Throughout the years learning, I got chatting to other late-to-education students as well as to the lecturers, and was inspired to look more seriously at undertaking a 'health related' science degree. Annoyingly, I was to fail the biology exam, although, in my defence, I believe this was due to my interest almost exclusively being in the 'human' module — I cared little for the other biological sciences. Nonetheless, I was not deterred from further studying.

I scrolled through a huge array of acclaimed, if not officially substantiated, 'alternative therapy' prospectuses, which seemed to be less focussed on the 'why' and more absorbed in the 'what'. To me, osteopathy, chiropractic and physiotherapy looked by far the most credible — and I would be able to study to degree level. Initially, I was tempted by a three- year physiotherapy degree in Bristol, but it turned out to be a full-time course — and that was not an option for me.

So, abandoning my husband (he had just had a vasectomy and was not a happy chappy), my eleven-year-old son and my eight-year-old daughter in our St. Austell home, I set off for London and my secured interview with The College of Osteopaths (COET - est. 1948) at

Middlesex University in North London. I thought I would kick back and have a pleasant and restful journey and took the coach (bad idea in hindsight.) The seven hour endurance test that was National Express succeeded in causing an acute case of what I now know to be *piriformis hypertonia* - I had squeezed the life out of my sciatic nerve, a tendency I had suffered on and off since the age of 19. Luckily, of course, I was in the perfect place for presenting with such a condition and was promptly 'demonstrated' upon, to the delight of the other interviewees – and to my own considerable relief.

By the end of my interview, I knew that I had secured a place, even though I had no 'real' qualifications. I'm still not convinced that it should be so easy. However, the point is that, in taking on mature students, the college was not necessarily looking for 'academics' but rather for life experience and an appetite to learn. I ticked these boxes; the only thing I didn't possess was a science background.

I spent five years at Middlesex University on an extended pathway degree. My real 'clinic' time was spent at the COET in Borehamwood, Hertfordshire. The first three years were part-time, while the final two became increasingly full-time. It was in your interest to make the extra commitment; failure would not come cheap.

And yet the degree was deemed part-time by the government, so student loans were not available for this 'pathway of learning' at that time. Consequently, the annual £5,000 fee was picked up by yours truly for five years. Somehow, too, I had forgotten to factor in travelling expenses. I was to-ing and fro-ing from Cornwall to London once, sometimes twice, a week, using various modes of transport, including the pseudo overnight 'sleeper', and leaving my husband and children with a list of *do's* and *don'ts* as long as the Tamar Bridge - I hate to think how many visits they paid to *McDonald's*, how often they went to school in dirty shirts, or how many hours they spent on the *Play Station*. On top of all this, I had to find the wherewithal for food, books, clothing and accommodation. Most, if not all, of my colleagues put me up – and put up with me - at some time or other. Thank you, Cohort F. And I resumed a long-overdue relationship with my wonderful cousin, Wendy, as I dossed down for a time at her house on the outskirts of London, and begged the occasional bed in the homes of my sister and sister-in-law. Seriously, thank you, every one of you.

As if this wasn't punishing enough - the itinerant lifestyle, not dossing down with Wendy - at the end of Year Three I had a really bright idea. I said to my husband *"Do you know what? I'm a bit fed up of Cornwall, let's move to Spain"*. His response? Incredibly, he said: *"You only live once"* and, six months later, in July 2004, we were ensconced in Iznajar, a tiny rural olive farming community in the province of Cordoba, southern Spain.

And so, three years into my training, I found myself in a house with no electricity, running water or mains drainage – not even a lav - learning to speak with a southern Spanish drawl, trying to carve out a niche in the Andalucían massage market and travelling humongous distances, at outrageous cost, backwards and forwards to London every week. This is truly another book in the making, (although, I think it's probably been done to death …..).

I look back on my study years with equal measures of affection and horror. We had a rather exceptional class, with students from all walks of life and various high flying careers already under their belt, but just 15 of us, the smallest cohort for years, apparently. Most of us were mature students with families, and it was a very long and arduous slog for us all. I was a long way from my home and family and the course took an inevitable toll on our wallets. Although, with some students travelling from France, Germany and other EU countries, I was not the most 'travelled' student in the College. By the time Year Five had come to an end, I had run up debts of well over £60,000. You may think that wasn't such a bad price to pay by today's standards. I'll let you know when I've finished paying.....

My family unit suffered from lack of good old fashioned quality time and my marriage barely survived – I'm exceptionally glad it did. Friends? Social life? I wasn't really sure what they were by the time I finally surfaced and crawled out of my 'o' zone – (poor attempt at osteopathic humour). However, I confess that I spent an inordinate amount of time making up for it afterwards. Post graduate celebrations comprised a whirlwind trip to Rome with my husband and cousin Wendy, where, in the swanky Italian shops, we kitted ourselves out with appropriate attire for the Graduation Ball. We all 'did' a lot of glam, food and savouring the wonder that is Rome. A few months later I joined an East Coast America '60s themed band, mischievously entitled *Beaver Patrol*, as one of the vocalists and learned to play basic acoustic guitar – well, five years *is* a long time with your head in a hole....

I recently had a clear-out at home and came across some of the bountiful notes my children wrote to me while I was away. Always considerate and caring, hoping I'm okay and *'missing you'*. I owe them so much. Not so long ago, my daughter, now a mother herself, confided to me how she hated it when I wasn't there and she recalled telling my husband, in temper, that she hated him; it had left him in tears. Naturally, she's mortified at the memory now, and she, my son and my husband are, thankfully, all very close today. What a sacrifice they made for me.

My own self-belief went up and down like a yo-yo; I've always pushed myself but this was on an astronomical scale and I don't think anything I ever do again will match it; although, I about to undertake a degree in astrobiology .... just don't tell my husband!

I clearly remember, towards the end of Year Five, being asked by lecturers to attend the University's Open Day, to encourage the new intake. It was the promise of food that swung it for us, but, as I scoffed the vol-au-vents and sandwiches, I had to swallow the urge to scream, at the top of my lungs, *"Don't do it!"*

Chapter 3:   Back to School

We all realised very early on that we were going to be doing a lot of stripping off during our five years of training. In our first year we all became accustomed to taking our clothes off and pointing at each other's bodies, looking for clues as to what the hell osteopathy was all about.   We all developed quirky *do's, don'ts, will's* and *won'ts*, when it came to taking our clothes off in front of each other..... I confess to being initially blasé as an enthusiastic first year, but as the years passed volunteered my body less and less. I also began to behold the human form very differently to how I had perceived it previously. I'll even go as far as to say that the 'magic' was stolen from me. I now look at a passer-by, and think *"He's going to struggle in ten years"*, or *"Sit up straight, woman."* I really can't help it.

At some point during these early months, I recall one of our lecturers informing us 'first years' that, before to the end of Year Five, we would all have to undertake 'coccyx adjustment' training.... the internal one, or *per rectum*, as it is correctly termed. We laughed hysterically at the thought, and made plans as to how we were going to approach this when the time came - we'd learned already that all 'practice' was carried out on each other. My word, did those five years fly by.

All too soon we were ensconced in the 'visceral' lecture, (learning about treatment of the internal organs), and being asked to pair up with a consenting colleague. We were all a little fraught, to say the least, and clandestinely plotted among ourselves how to survive it with as much dignity as we could muster. We'd had years to prepare, right down to the last tiny detail. My colleague and I promised each other that, whichever one of us found herself on the couch first; the other would cover her backside with a strategically placed towel and then just, well, kind of feel her way in?

Regrettably, of course, our lecturer was not party to this plan so, when my partner jumped on to the treatment table, turned on her side and thrust her posterior towards me to be discreetly covered, he whipped off the towel, declaring *"Right! Now the first thing you have to do is part the cheeks"*. Which he duly did...

I tried not to ask **too** many questions during this critical part of the procedure, out of consideration for my partner, you understand, but, well, quite frankly, my curiosity was piqued, and, if not then, when....?

I recounted the story to this particular lecturer at a conference some years later and he did chuckle a bit. I should admit, too, that the technique we learned has come in handy (chortle, chortle) on more than one occasion when patients were (almost) glad of my selfless learning, each of them unfortunately having to succumb to the internal coccyx adjustment technique. One young lady had fallen backwards on to a wheelbarrow handle ouch. Whilst there was a young man whose 'friends', on a drunken weekend 'stag' celebration, thought it would be amusing to tie him to a fallen tree on woodland near Truro, and leave him. In his desperate attempt to free himself he managed to partially impale his bottom on a broken branch. I'll leave the rest, and the details of his two visits to my clinic, to your imagination.

On a more serious note, it is worth pointing out that, if this procedure is suggested in clinic by your practitioner, you need to be 100% certain that he/she is registered, and remember: all practitioners are obliged to ask you to sign a consent form...

From coccyx adjustment, that lecture moved straight on to 'prostate milking' (obviously not mine...) According to the *Prostate Health Centre* website, prostates are 'milked' because: a) it enables easier passage of urine through the urinary tract (albeit temporarily) and b) it reduces the incidence of an enlarged prostate.   Neither of these assumed benefits appears to be supported by EBM and there are those who believe the procedure can actually increase incidence of prostate cancer (again, no evidence). Whatever the case, it is undoubtedly a controversial procedure. I certainly couldn't see myself as a prostate 'milker' so, along with many others, I opted out of that practical lecture.

Visceral osteopathy* is the name given to the category that the prostate and coccyx procedures fall into, and there are lots more of your 'insides' that osteopathy can access and treat. It involves working with or on internal organs and other viscera such as the liver, digestive system, lungs and reproductive organs, and often the diaphragm.

*True viscera do not include the coccyx or diaphragm, but for ease of lecture planning, techniques of the 'insides' were taught in the visceral lecture time.

Many osteopaths work on the diaphragm, which, while not viscera itself, comprises muscle and tendon and has a large influence on lung function.

Due to its skeletal attachments, it can give rise to discomfort in the upper lumbar spine region and it can be 'accessed' and treated here, in the cervical spine (neck), and directly under the rib cage, as well as through deep breathing activity. Our objective is to calm muscle spasm through stretching and breathing techniques, thus assisting in the restoration of optimal diaphragmatic function. As well as manual stretching, other exercises can be given to help with this type of problem, essentially aiming at increasing blood/oxygen to muscle tendons and viscera.

When one of my regular patients, a man in his 60s, with a long history of spinal surgery, turned up on one occasion complaining of a back spasm, he was astonished to

learn that there was no problem with his lumbar spine but that his diaphragm had 'spasmed', affecting other local muscle groups which attach to the lower extremities (below the waist). He had recently joined a local choir and had thrown himself whole-heartedly (and seemingly 'diaphragmatically') into a new singing 'career'. *"Don't tell me I've got to stop?"* he asked, horror- stricken. I reassured him: *"The more you sing, the better your body will accommodate it"*, (as with most exercise). He presented himself at his next practice, proudly claiming to be the first member of the choir to have suffered a 'singing injury'.

I personally don't do too much direct visceral work (as in organs). However, I regularly provide advice and treatment for patients who have been under the knife and whose body is dealing with adhesions (internal scar tissue).

Scarring can cause as many problems on the inside as it does on the surface of the skin, and usually takes a while longer to recover and heal optimally. Scar tissue *per se* is poorly oxygenated because it is very fibrous and is insufficiently supplied with blood pathways (arterioles and the like.) and so it needs all the help it can get to encourage good blood/oxygen flow.

In other words, regular blood flow means better joint movement. Think of blood as being similar to that of engine oil, which requires regular flow at an ambient temperature for optimal performance.   But it is not just a question of a quick visit to an osteopath, physiotherapist, chiropractor or massage therapist for a 'top up' - it obviously helps to work on the tissue daily.   After any kind of surgery, you should be seeking immediate advice on self-treatment and care for the acute, or early, stage of the scar to encourage repair.

An interesting example of how scarring can affect a 'system' of the body – in this case the respiratory system - presented itself in my fourth year.   A 27-year-old male patient attended clinic with a cervical spine (neck) muscle spasm. He was a swimming pool installation technician who was very fond of the gym and, in particular, the weights; overall quite a fit chap. Further questioning revealed that, over a period of some six years, he had suffered no fewer than nine spontaneous *pneumothoraces* (collapsing lung), six on the left and three on the right. And he had no medical explanation. However, when questioned about his respiratory health, he did admit to suffering persistent cold or chest infections of one description or another, and to being almost permanently on antibiotics - highly unusual for a 'fit' young man.

As a student, I was required to present a patient's case history to a clinician for discussion prior to any examination. Having done so, I returned to the room and asked the patient to undress to his underwear. (Yes, I know it was a neck complaint - more on this subject later). On his upper torso I immediately observed a very thick scar, which looked to have been caused by a burn. It ran from the front left upper area (over his heart, lung and collar bone) down to the bottom of the left rib cage, almost covering the whole of the back of his *scapula* (shoulder blade).

On enquiring as to the origins of the scarring, I learned that, when he was a toddler, his mother had spilled scalding coffee over him and had reacted by ripping his clothing off him. At this point, though, I was getting the distinct impression that he did not want to discuss the matter any further, a position I respected entirely. However, I'd learned enough to have a pretty good idea as to why his respiratory function was struggling. With the tissues surrounding the lungs already strained and scarred, he was likely to be tipping the balance with his persistent heavy weight lifting. It took three treatments to correct his cervical spine complaint, and that was where we left it.

Why was all of this information relevant? Because no osteopath in our clinic would have dreamt of risking another *pneumothorax* by delivering a high velocity thrust technique to his thoracic (mid spine), or indeed to any other part of the spine, I hope (this controversial technique is discussed in chapter 11). The point is that we needed to discover the information in order to determine what type of treatment this man could and could not have.

The effects of internal scarring were never clearer to me than in the case of a 30-year-old patient undergoing a *micro-discectomy* (partial disc removal) at which I was fortunate enough to be present a few years into my career. These operations are not done lightly and are incredibly costly. In this case, I think consideration was shown because of his age and the impact it was having on his daily life. I clearly remember the first procedure. The surgeon considerately identified all relevant soft tissue for me (no-one else in the room was that interested - it was just 'a day in the life of') as he skilfully picked his way through to the offending disc. Unfortunately, the procedure was not a success and, six months later, he was back for another attempt. When the surgeon re-opened his pathway there was virtually no identifiable tissue at all. It looked like one homogenous mass of scarring – very difficult for the surgeon, but very revealing for me, in terms of the impact the scar will have on his future mobility. Scarring exists in order to help strengthen the piece of anatomy that is 'broken'. But it reduces range of movement and circulation.

As 'first years' we continually practised our palpation skills, feeling tissues and anomalies with our hands. We'd be asked to find one 'promontory' (bony landmark) or another and I distinctly remember feeling utterly useless, unable to find or feel anything apart from skin. To be honest, to begin with, I would just lie, saying, *'Oh yes, there's the transverse process of blah blah,'* while loosely brushing my fingertips over the said area of surface anatomy.

As time went by, though, I came to realise that this is a rare skill, invaluable in helping reach a diagnosis and one that I should seek to improve. It must be similar, I have always thought, to that developed by blind and partially-sighted people, who use touch to identify objects. We were taught so thoroughly to feel what is 'normal' or 'text book', and to compare right and left, good side and offending side, that it now doesn't feel like a learned skill at all, rather like a natural instinct, such as swimming or riding a bike. I never tire of the satisfaction I get from what it reveals, though. It is, I believe, one of the distinguishing features of osteopathic evaluation.

Our lectures took place at weekends, at the Archway campus of Middlesex University. We also had to undertake 1,200 clinical hours over our five years and, from Year Three onwards, we were let loose on real live patients.

The COET was situated just down the road from the Borehamwood and Elstree studios, and was visited by the odd 'celeb' from '*Holby City*' and '*Eastenders*'. I happened to be there on one such occasion, which saw a 'doctor' from *Holby City* admitted to the clinic with an obvious back problem, apparently incurred on set while filming a lift shaft escape scene. She was shepherded in by her entourage, each of them brandishing what seemed like at least three mobile phones, and insisting that she must return to finish filming that evening. The clinician on duty that day was one of my favourites, an Australian chap with a wicked sense of humour and no time whatsoever for what he regarded as 'prime time' British television piffle. He entered the room demanding to know why there were so many people present. On being enlightened, he proclaimed never to have seen the show and promptly shoo'ed them all out. He then examined the starlet and declared it was likely that she had had a *mild disc protrusion*, or possibly an *annular tear*, and added that she should not be expected to return to the set. As he set about strapping up her lumbar spine to prevent excess movement, I made my way to the door, but not before I heard her sigh, "Oh I wish I could be strapped up like this to get into my dress for the BAFTAs.....'

There was an unmistakable pecking order in clinic, although, as 'first years', we didn't actually rank at all. And if we *dared* to get a question correct that a higher ranking student couldn't answer, well, that was profanity itself, as I found out more than once. I'm really not one of the *'Please sir, pick me'* brigade - it's just that I'm the kind of person who, when I KNOW I'm right (which wasn't often, as I happened to be in one of the College's brightest cohorts for some time), I want everyone to know I know!

One or two of my fellow students had 'jumped ship' from allied professions and, among the newly-arrived 'first years', as I moved into my second year, happened to be the lead physiotherapist of Manchester City Football Club, whose knowledge and experience probably surpassed that of even the brightest fifth year students. Very few of us were ever confident in his presence – gracious though you always were, Jim.

Some of the clinicians were sticklers for presentation and I was often picked out on 'roll call' as a scruffy 'oik'. My white coats were wrong, my hair in my face, my name badge missing. It was quite mortifying to be told, at the age of 33, to 'sort out your appearance'. Our devoted receptionist/agony aunt/surrogate mother/covert operations manager was forever seeing to one teary eyed student or another - and I was no exception.

However, I can truthfully say, hand on heart, that I liked and got on well with all of our lecturers and clinicians. One or two of them, and they will *know* who they are, were a little scary to start with, but, once we began to roll with the punches we became accustomed to their dark, warped minds... I thank you wonderful ladies and gents.

During our first two years we spent hour after hour observing more senior students carrying out examinations and treatments. However, at the end of the second year, as soon as the current crop of 'fifth years' had passed their final clinical competence exams (FCCs), and fled Hertfordshire, throwing their white clinic coats to the wind, we were allowed to actually treat patients - a full three months before our time. Now we could be revered by the first year students - who, of course, by now were thinking of themselves as second year students....

Much later, in Year Four, we had the opportunity to spend time observing and participating in human dissection, which, whilst both a privilege and a remarkable opportunity, was also a little scary. I shall never forget the look of horror on one colleague's face as the lecturer in the dissection room, explaining the role and depth of the *retinaculum* (large fibrous strap in the wrist), reached under the sheet, pulled out an arm and thrust it towards him. We all became accustomed eventually, but this was a defining moment in my training, as I proved to myself that I wasn't too delicate to take part. Indeed, I was confident enough subsequently to attend a number of surgical procedures, with the kind permission of patients and consultants. In fact, my love of human anatomy peaked in the operating theatre; there is without doubt no better way to study it than in a live procedure.

I spent a couple of hours last Christmas observing a total knee replacement of a patient of mine that both she and the surgeon allowed me to attend (as happens for me quite a lot). The entire procedure was a very svelte and mastered operation undertaken to the melodic upbeats of Michael Bubles' Christmas offering. The whole procedure played out rather like a rhythmic sketch from the Two Ronnies, the whole team were bobbing up and down throughout. I have never seen a slicker team.

My second year was also memorable for the chance we had to visit Gunther von Hagens' *'Bodyworks'* project in London's Brick Lane. Von Hagens had invented the 'human plastination' technique for preserving and displaying biological tissue and we were captivated by what we saw. The exhibition was the subject of much debate, and even threatened with sabotage, so security was very heavy. I was warned on more than enough occasions to curb my enthusiasm as I continually leaned over the glass display cabinets...

Von Hagens' work remains controversial even today and is questioned by many who claim it is sensationalist and even degrading. Personally, I think he is a very clever educator who has done much to raise awareness of many modern day illnesses such as diabetes, and other obesity related disease. Yes, he's an eccentric, who wears a hat whilst he dissects, but, in my view, he will be remembered in history as one of the worlds pioneering anatomists.

The history of anatomy is laced with stories of skulduggery and murder. Who hasn't heard of Edinburgh's notorious Burke and Hare? Fortunately, we no longer have the cadaver supply shortage that existed in 19th century Britain, but, when judging Von Hagens' approach to our edification, we can be all too quick to forget the part played by these salacious historical events in the progress made by science and medicine. In today's society, we're 'ok' with 'reality television', which fills our evenings with images of fat fetishes, and advertisements for fatty foods, but, when faced with factual programmes exploring the consequences of over-eating/drinking, we all tend to get upset.

By practising techniques on each other during practical lectures we discovered things we never knew about ourselves... such as the odd *scoliosis* ('*c*' or '*s*' shaped bend in the spine) or leg length difference, and we each became the proud owners of 'anomalies' and 'artefacts'. Some entertaining mnemonics were passed down from student to student for remembering anatomical parts of the body, such as:

Proper Anatomical Name	Little Reminders
Valves of the heart:	
Mitral	my
tricuspid	tits
aortic	are
pulmonary	perfect
Bones of the carpus (hand)	
Scaphoid	scared
Lunate	lovers
triquetrium	try
pisiform	positions
trapezium	that
trapezoid	they

capitate	cannot
hamate	handle

Cranial Nerves

Olfactory	oh
Optic	oh
Ophthalmic	oh
Trochlear	to
Trigeminal	touch
Abducent	and
Facial	feel
Vestibulochoclear	various
Glossopharyngeal	girls
Vagus	vaginas
Accessory	are
Hypoglossal	hairy

I think you can see where this is going... Although unable to take books and study aids into our exams, we could not be prevented from taking our own bodies, and you would often catch colleagues pointing at themselves while silently reciting these wonderful mantras.

Chapter 4:   Cutting the Mustard

For five solid years, we were continually tested and re-tested. Failure really was not an option.   If you failed one year, you didn't move to the next and would be forced to re-take that year until you were successful; for some, this was many times over.

We were endlessly assessed in clinic and, both with written exams and practical, both mock (to estimate our shortcomings) and real (to ensure we met the standard for the end of year exams). I actually learned not to be nervous of exams and eventually took them in my stride, allowing very little to stress me out. I regularly shared the ten-hour return journey to university with a colleague and we talked of little other than anatomy, physiology etc. This repetition was my saviour (thanks, Chris). During year five, I stayed with other students in my class and at the end of a day at clinic/lecture, we talked nothing but revision. Don't get me wrong, we had a party or two –and trainee osteopaths under the influence are, to say the very least, a little scary...

Then, at the very end of our training, we faced our Final Clinical Competency exams

(FCCs). Among many other things, this involved treating a new patient, comprising a case history procedure, considering the possible causes and discussing the examination, results and intended treatment plan with a clinician. This all sounds very straightforward, I hear you say. In normal circumstances it might be, but here it is all done in front of a 'firing squad' of external adjudicators who are grilling you throughout the entire sweaty process.

My patient arrived and was shown to the treatment room, where I began taking her case history. I let out a breath and concluded that this was going to be a non-complicated new patient and that, in all likelihood she was suffering with classic osteo-arthritic cervical spine (neck) pain. I was then joined by no fewer than four adjudicators (two internal, representing the college, and two external, from GOsC). All four took seats on the other side of the room, from where they watched and listened as intently as if they were filming an Attenborough documentary. I was taking everything in my stride and things seemed to be going really well until suddenly, and without warning, my patient burst into tears. Over the next few minutes, between sobs, I learned that she had lost her husband just three months previously, and that, only two weeks before her visit, her brother had been murdered! Consequently, she was feeling, ahem, well, rather fraught. It took me some time to calm her down and she was still quivering when I finally left the room, followed, one by one, by a rather disconcerted bunch of adjudicators.

Strangely, at this point, I instinctively knew I had passed. Not because I am cocksure by nature - I was rarely sure of anything during those five years - but because I was in no doubt that I had said and done all the right things for this particular patient. I went through the usual procedure of presenting my case, treating the patient and determining what future management she would need; it all became a blur by the time I finally handed in my paperwork for scrutiny and further questioning.

So, when I went upstairs to throw *my* white clinic coat to the wind and head for home, I wore a quiet smile of satisfaction, in the knowledge that it was done and that I had qualified. I like to think my treatment played a rather critical role although I still had to face a grilling for what seemed like a life-time. But confirmation of my qualification came via a phone call some seven hours later (not that I was counting...).

Chapter 5:   Let Me At 'Em!

By the time I left University I was classed as a safe practitioner, but I still lacked immensely in confidence. In the days before the work we do was accredited with degree status, osteopaths learned by spending time under the watchful eye of a 'Grandma/pa' practitioner, until they were ready to spread their wings. It is still common practice for junior medical professionals to be placed with more senior and experienced doctors and nurses for a few years after qualifying. But osteopaths no longer have the same opportunity to 'understudy'. Nor are we graded in the way that medical staff are, i.e. we are unable to aspire to the heights of more senior or specialist consultant, (although this may change in the future).

I personally think we should, if desired, be able to 'rank' within our profession, if only to specialise; but with our current system of regulation, this will likely prove to be a convoluted and expensive journey and we will be recognised as specialist or senior only among ourselves and not by the wider medical/caring communities.   At   present,   because   we commission our work privately, any osteopath or chiropractor, or for that matter private physiotherapist, can label themselves 'consultant' or 'specialist'. But then, so can a sock salesman. This is precisely *why* we need to grade our profession.

These days we are turned out fresh faced and eager to impress upon the world - well actually lots of us were just knackered and never wanting to pick up another Goodman and Snyder (the manual therapists' bible) ever again... and free to join an established practice anywhere, or even set up on our own, as a fully-fledged practitioner.

And that's what I did, promptly setting up my own practice at home in the West Country. My entire practical experience consisted of only a few dozen patients that my 'massage therapy' qualification had allowed me to treat at home, practical lectures and 1,200 hours of clinic time. But, when I had come to re-write my 'myself as an osteopath' assignment at the end of Year Five, as we were asked to, I had known that I had earned my title, that I *was* a safe practitioner and that I now knew maybe a little of what I wanted or hoped to achieve in the real world.

My initial reaction to qualifying was numbness and a realisation that time existed again. I had become so unaccustomed to having time that it actually unsettled me for the first few months and I was unsure how to structure my day. It goes without saying that any practice needs building, and that this takes time, but I threw myself into the task at such a fury that, within six months, I was inundated.

Practising in the real world is, of course, a vastly different proposition to operating in the cocooned environment in which we had learned. For all my training, I still had my doubts, particularly when it came to communicating to the wider medical community. I would regularly question myself about what I was doing. But, as the months passed, I realized that it is in the real world that most of your learning is done, when all the theory is put into practice on a daily basis. I called on my lecturers and clinicians quite a few times in my first year 'out there', but things gradually became easier; I got to grips with the terminology, found a niche within my local community and began to feel a growing modicum of confidence. And I gradually found myself able to explain complex conditions to patients in a way that was easily understood, rather than in the intricate and convoluted medical jargon that I had learned in the classroom.

I still feel there is room for some kind of phasing-in procedure or probationary period that newly qualified practitioners should go through, in order to help them acclimatise.

What Are You Looking At?

When patients arrive, they are invariably in pain and regularly incoherent. Information is often garbled so, although we make a point of listening to their main concerns, we all follow a fairly strict protocol of questioning in order to form a working diagnosis. However, a diagnosis is often not possible at the initial consultation and patients will often need to return for a re-assessment. As a matter of fact I try not to make any form of diagnosis in the first few weeks of treating a patient, (provided, of course, that they *need* a few weeks of treatment), as long as I am clear that I am not dealing with a red flag or reason to refer to a GP. This is understandably frustrating for those who want to go home or back to work and tell family, friends, colleagues and employer the cause of their pain. Notwithstanding, it is important not to jump to conclusions after a one hour treatment session; patients cannot possibly tell you all you need to know, and vice versa, in such a short space of time. Having said that, of course, many patients only need one visit, in which case they are followed up with a phone call in order to update their patient notes. Life is varied.

We use the same orthopaedic and neurological assessment and examination methods as would your GP or consultant to filter the three or four most likely causes, what we call our 'differentials', while ruling out red flags and referrals to other professions. We also undertake a postural assessment, check the function and range of joints and try to ascertain how the pain occurred or developed. Often, the how and why are glaringly obvious to all. Sometimes though, the process of pain has been accumulative, due perhaps to repetitive action or occupational wear and tear, and needs a little more 'unpicking'.

A recent classic example of this presented with a patient I had treated episodically for many years. She hadn't needed treatment for about 18 months, however, when she turned up again with her usual cervical spine complaint. But she also happened to mention that she was experiencing pain in the breast/pectoral side of her right arm. There were clear signs of *pectoralis* and tightening of the *rotator cuff* (upper arm muscles and tendons) on one side. But no explanation could be provided by the patient. Finally, I was forced to physically show her the position that the body needed to be in to create such tension. Whereupon she suddenly piped up: *'Oh yes, I've taken up crochet'*...

When assessing patients, we do more than just evaluate the site of pain. Osteopaths are often looking for asymmetry, or irregularity of the body. Most of us are born fairly symmetrical and develop over-use or under-use 'adjustments' as we grow and age. The body is more than capable at making up for functions which are injured or not working properly and we have an eye for these 'compensation patterns', too. So we look to enhance these functions maximally at the same time, as well as treating the 'painful bit'. This learned method often puts us one step ahead of many other manual therapy treatment programmes, which tend to focus solely on the area that hurts, allowing vital information regarding the whole body often to be missed. When combined with our patient case histories, which take into account, not only sports participation and occupational stresses/hours of work, but also posture, previous health issues and family commitments, you can see why we have a pretty good recipe for treating the *person*. This is often termed 'holistic', which, in my view is one of the most over-used terms in health care today. I prefer to think of it as a complete care package (with or without medicine), with honest, realistic and achievable objectives. And (in my case) definitely no sorcery, crystals or energy aligning....

Whilst we learn from text books and tutorials, we very rarely apply their teachings in their entirety. This is because patients very rarely present as 'text book' cases.

As well as palpation, experience itself enables us to determine very quickly where to look. Soft tissue that is under pressure due to inflammation or repetitive strain is normally obvious to an osteopath; it is often constricted and tight and reveals itself in normal everyday movements, known as 'restricted range of movement', or can be hot and swollen.

Musculoskeletal abnormality can be obvious to a trained eye. It may be due to underlying joint restrictions or to muscular and/or ligamentous tension. It is not unusual for a patient to be uncertain of when the pain began, or of its cause. Our bodies can 'dawdle' a little when sending signals to the brain. The brain says "go, go, go", but sometimes the body response is slow, slow, slow. Certain tissue can counter this sluggishness by tightening up and this is a very common occurrence. Getting out of bed, gardening, shopping, picking something up from the floor – all can result in what we see in our clinics all day, every day.

While we are no substitute for Accident and Emergency Departments, at least 40% of my work presents as an emergency. Of this, many cases will involve muscle 'spasm' (tight and painful muscles). So what exactly *happens* when a muscle is said to have gone into spasm? The usual cause is often a sudden, rapid movement, particularly after we have been resting, sitting, sleeping, etc. Or a repetitive action such as gardening or lifting. While our muscles themselves can respond quickly enough to a command from the brain, our ligaments as we age become less efficient at 'computing' the information, and the mixed messages lead to conflict, which results in a painful tightening of the muscles. This is designed to slow us down and prevent excessive movement, and most of the time it does a good job of this. However, as we get older, our tissue reaction times tend to slow down due to poorer circulation and 'spasming' can happen more readily.

This type of injury is incredibly common. Repetition of certain activities can cause muscle tightening, so, for example, if you've been digging for hours in the garden - and it's not an everyday activity - you can experience a gradual tightening of muscle and other soft tissue. This often rectifies itself with no help whatsoever from manual therapy.

When it doesn't, our role is to assess joints of the body, comparing good with bad, which positions cause pain and which do not. Many osteopaths now rely on technology, such as ultrasound, to treat patients, but most of us still use observation and palpation to assess them.

I have already touched on our skill in 'feeling' what is wrong with a patient. Surface tissue usually provides clues as to what is happening beneath the skin. Inflamed tissue will obviously feel hot, while colder areas can imply poor circulation to the joint and soft tissue, and can indicate circulatory disease.   But the areas of the body which act as lymphatic drainage and artillery sites, such as the *inguinal* (groin) and the scalene muscles at the side of the neck, can signal whether or not the body is struggling to cope with infection. The skin can give clues to nutritional deficiency, by changing colour (pigmentation), becoming scaly or 'dimpling' and it can over- or under-produce sweat, suggesting that the sympathetic nervous system ('fight or flight') may be under-or over-performing.

All of this can be detected by our palpation techniques, which can also determine whether tissue is 'moving' well, or whether it feels 'solid', signifying possible damage. Dysfunctional areas of the musculoskeletal system often feel constricted and hot, and are in a phase of spasm. Tissue which has been in this state for many months or years, however, - termed as chronic - tends to feel very fibrous due to being poorly supplied with blood/oxygen flow, and therefore can feel cold in comparison to the normal heat of the opposite limb/body part.

Another, less indecorous, mnemonic defines what we are feeling in our fingers and seeing with our eyes when we look for clues as to what's happening in a patient's tissue.

T   Tenderness (to touch)
A   Asymmetry (why is it not symmetrical?)
R   Restrictions (joint/tissue movement or lack of)
T   Tissue Texture Changes (often due to poor blood or nerve supply)

So, hopefully you now know what we are looking at, it just begs the question, what can we treat?

Chapter 6:   What Can We Treat...?

There is a chasm between what we are capable of treating and what we can legally advertise. For example, if I were to claim that I had 'cured' a lady of her nine- month insomnia problem, I would risk a fine by the Advertising Standards Authority (ASA). And yet .... the lady in question arrived complaining of a two-week-old pain in her shoulder - she just happened to be suffering with insomnia at that time. My job was to relieve the tension in her upper extremity musculoskeletal system, which I did. I did not set out to cure her insomnia. However, over the ensuing weeks she experienced a 95% improvement in her sleep pattern which, I believe, was simply due to a combination of having the time and a sympathetic ear during her treatment and a boost to her circulatory system which helped improve tissue tensions/dysfunctions and blood/oxygen flow. Placebo? Cataclysmic claim? Or utter rubbish? You decide.

The ASA is adamant on the question of testimonial evidence as substantiation in health matters. According to its website, it is unacceptable. It is also very clear when it comes to the provision of supporting research when making claims to cure or treat any illness, dysfunction or disease, and will and does prosecute.

Until recently, it was illegal for anyone other than manufacturers of researched medications to claim they could cure or treat headaches. As we are not a part of a multi-million pound industry like our pharmaceutical friends, it has taken us some time to provide evidence that manual therapy *can* benefit headache sufferers.

We have at last provided evidence to reverse the long-standing perception that the only plausible cure for a headache is to pop a pill in your mouth. Virtually all headache research used to be industry fuelled and funded, of course..

I chose not to advertise (except with the GOsC) and so my work presents via word of mouth, or referral by GP or other healthcare practitioner. However, what I do know through patient feedback is that I have relieved many patients of tension type headaches, hypoxic headaches (poor blood/oxygen flow to the brain), sinus headaches … the list goes on.

Headaches are a complicated subject; their aetiology (causation) is often far from understood, due to the complexity of the brain and its many functions. We do know that they are often initiated by stress and tension (remember the advert for Anadin? *"Headache? Tense, nervous headache?"*) and can signify raised blood pressure which, as we all know, can lead to stroke and myocardial infarction etc.

Stress alone can bring on a headache, precipitating a rise in blood pressure, making your arteries, arterioles and capillaries work and 'pump' harder and faster. Muscle tension, too, can contribute to a headache, putting a 'squeeze' on some of the soft tissues and nerves around the head, neck and shoulders, and leading to a reduction of blood/oxygen flow to the brain – termed 'hypoxia'. Osteopaths treat these tissues every day.

Another contentious condition is asthma, which hit the headlines in 2008 when the *British Chiropractic Association* sued *The Guardian*'s science writer, Simon Singh, over an article questioning claims of efficacy in the treatment of infantile colic and asthma. At the time many manual therapists were promoting themselves as being able to treat these particular illnesses, but the evidence was thin on the ground – as it is in all manual therapy.

Singh was alleged to have implied that members of the BCA knowingly promoted what he called *"bogus treatments"*. The Association eventually dropped its libel action, but only after the case had become a *cause celebre*, with scientists, celebrities and freedom of speech campaigners lining up to condemn the British libel laws and argue that Singh had a right to express his opinion in print.

Court of Appeal judges Lord Justice Judge, Lord Justice Neuberger and Lord Justice Sedley were later to rule: "*this litigation has almost certainly had a chilling effect on public debate which might otherwise have assisted potential patients to make informed choices about the possible use of chiropractic.*"   In my opinion, Mr. Singh was entirely right to question the original claim, and any other where evidence is non-existing or in its infancy.   Medications have the same restriction placed upon them.

And yet...some asthma patients *do* feel notable benefit from osteopathic, physiotherapy or chiropractic treatment.   Clearly, I am not talking about *'bone crunching'* techniques here - manual treatment is much more than that, as I hope is becoming clear. We provide sensible advice on lifestyle, occupation, breathing exercises, smoking cessation, weight issues and exercise, all asthma-related issues. We apply the same the same procedures as a physiotherapist in a hospital aiming to improve the lung function of a COPD (chronic obstructive pulmonary disease) patient. We have the same respiratory training. Medicine is a long way from curing asthma, and, until it can, shouldn't we manual therapists be allowed to assist wherever we can as part of an integrated approach?

Cochrane's Manual Therapy for Asthma research paper, 2009 review, which defines manual therapy as osteopathic, chiropractic and physiotherapy, concluded that *"there is insufficient evidence to support **or** refute the use of manual therapy for patients with asthma"* and suggests that *"larger scale studies be conducted"*. A similar research paper, entitled *'Breathing Exercises for Asthma'* concludes virtually the same. Yet, the *Chartered Society of Physiotherapists* website positively states, at the time of writing, that they can help you *"manage asthma"*, and "a consultation with a physio for asthma is likely to include breathing exercises".

I'm playing devil's advocate here, but is *'manage asthma'* an acceptable claim?

Today, NHS guidelines for the non-pharmacological management of asthma suggest acupuncture, Chinese herbal medicines and homeopathy, among others, may be of some help - even though they go on to say *"there is little evidence to suggest they work"*. There is, in fact, NO evidence-based research in existence *at all,* that homeopathy works. And the NHS is categorical in stating that there is no evidence at all to suggest spinal manipulation, manual therapy and massage is effective. It does, however, support the use of yoga, breathing exercises and the *Buteyko* (breathing therapy) technique.

This all paints a very confusing picture for the ASA, UK libel law makers and, not least, asthmatics.

We all need to take more care when making claims of efficacy, whatever our walk of life. The multiple facets of today's media frequently highlight unchecked claims of cures; hair growth, miracle supplements etc., often without censure and within the minutest limit of what is legal. We are bombarded daily with advertisements that we all know in reality are codswallop. *'Healthy'* cereals, *'low fat'* (often equating to horrifying amounts of sugar), the yoghurt which suddenly makes you beautiful (and laugh like a brainless buffoon), and my personal favourite, *'happy periods'*. Really? Who can honestly say they have *ever* had a happy period? And lo, we then enter the now huge and rather sad world of celebrity endorsement; being told 'we're worth it' but we need 'the London look', quite frankly makes me want to vomit. We are spoon-fed this superficial rot every day; no wonder we buy into the 'miracle pill/treatment' traps.

I realise that I am straying a little *'off piste'* here but, in my view, it is relevant; manual therapy often features 'multi-disciplinary' clinics/practices which can be far from immune from misleading the public. Here are just a couple of examples where efficacy claims are clearly being 'stretched'.

I found the following advert on a local internet site which promotes and informs women who have their own business - there are many others but these are particularly disturbing. It was from a *reiki* healer: *"Do you feel exhausted/drained/fearful? Then you are most probably living in a low frequency of energy. BUT don't worry"* (to the now very worried client whose frequency needs altering) – *"you can change this*!!!"

"I offer healing treatments, where this problem will be addressed and your vibrations raised. I work with universal energy that is in all of us, unblocking areas that are stagnant. " That is a heck of a lot of energy. Does she mean electromagnetic, kinetic or thermal? She then goes on to say: *"Healing has helped many physical problems including sciatica"* (not actually a condition), *"migraines"*, (no, no, no), *"M.E., bursitis"* (very clever indeed), *"numerous back problems"* (she probably can't think of any more because she only knows 'sciatica'). *"It also helps any mental or spiritual imbalance, creating a calmness and a strength that may have been lost along the way"* (I'm lost myself). *"To name a few, stress, addictions, anxiety, depression the list goes on and on".* This is all harmless, surely? No. It is a claim of biblical proportions. If she could do all she says we would have no need of medicine as we know it.

I did actually contact this lady to ask her to remove the advert, and she was most apologetic. She seemed to think that I was offended. I corrected her: it is simply illegal.

Then there was the following, which happened to me some years ago when I agreed to 'swap' a massage for a treatment on my feet by a reflexologist – a reciprocal arrangement popular among therapists. I was curious to know what reflexologists 'knew' and did. On examining my feet, however, she said: *"You have lots of calluses"*, which, of course, I already knew. She followed this up with: *"It's probably because you're stressed"*. I nearly fell off the couch laughing. Yes, calluses are caused by stress, but not the type of stress she was implying. Most calluses are formed by altered gait and over-pronation of the foot – (where the foot strikes and leaves the floor at a certain angle repeatedly, causing the body to lay down more skin over time).

I'm not saying that these therapies do not have a contribution to make to the world, just that they need to keep it real and honest. Even if you did succeed in curing a client of his hairy butt, if the evidence does not exist you cannot claim it.

The problem for me is that manual therapists tend to get lumped in with much of this claptrap.

Chapter 7: So What *Can* You Treat?

Our bodies are run by a pretty complex nervous system, which includes what is known as 'the sympathetic nervous system' - the bit that is often referred to as the 'flight or fight' response. When this part of the nervous system is over stimulated, whether through stress, anxiety, drugs, poor diet or disease, its functions can become a little overwhelmed and difficult to calm down, often resulting in pain and inflammation and sometimes infection and disease. Tightened musculature can reduce capillary blood flow and compress nerves and other soft tissue. This volatile nervous activity is referred to as over-facilitation and can result in everyday tension headaches, 'panic attacks', over/under stimulation of the heart, adrenal/kidney and liver function and raised blood pressure.

Modern medicine may use drugs such as neurogenics, beta blockers, non-steroidal anti-inflammatories (NSAIDS), low dose diazepam, etc. Often this is all that is needed to address the 'medical' problem. However, the stress and the soft tissue discomfort will not always have been addressed. Osteopaths aim to calm down this over-facilitation through various soft tissue techniques, which help reduce oedema (swelling) and inflammation. Often, being able to talk about the pain and work through how it occurred, helps patients understand what they can do to help themselves, by managing their stress levels. This is how medicine integrates with manual therapy.

Most people, when conjuring an image of an osteopath, think 'back', but in truth, whilst 70% of my work is spinal it's not all back, back, back. But, over the years, I've been confronted with a vast array of problems – nothing actually surprises me these days. One lady, for example, arrived complaining of 'tingling' and pain in the vulva (genital area) during sexual intercourse. This was an immediate 'red flag', because it would be reasonable to suspect some nerve root involvement or 'systemic' disease, and she was promptly despatched to the neurosurgeon. She was then seen by the dermatologist, who diagnosed *vulvodynia*, a chronic, painful condition of the vulva – most unpleasant. I'd never heard of it, it's fair to say, but she was quickly referred on to the NHS to explore treatment options.

I've also treated a number of people with jaw hypo-mobility (insufficient movement). One arrived, having come off decidedly the worse in a' fight' with her dentist while undergoing a wisdom tooth extraction. The dentist, unable seemingly to obtain sufficient purchase on the tooth, used the patient as leverage throughout the procedure. Despite considerable pushing and pulling, only three quarters of the tooth was extracted (the rest had to be removed at a later date) This lady subsequently began to suffer with headaches, drop fainting attacks, vertigo, nausea and lack of movement in the neck and the jaw. Results of an MRI scan of the upper cervical spine (neck) and brain stem later revealed a *chiari malformation,* which is a complication of the cerebral part of the brain, although it was unclear which of the four types of malformation she had. It is a fairly unusual condition, which, thanks to the increasing use of MRI scans, is detected more frequently these days. (*Type II chiari malformation* is often found in those with *spina bifida*). One citation on the *Neurology Journal* website actually pondered the relationship between *chiari malformation* and cervical spine manipulation (HVT). There is a possibility that the trauma of the dentistry may have caused my patient's symptoms. Fortunately, she was eventually to respond to stretching techniques and deep soft tissue work, but her symptoms remained for a long time.

No two days are alike. One poor fellow, who ran an animal sanctuary, had fallen down his concrete stairs, saving the dog he'd been clutching, but duly giving his coccyx something of a battering. Needless to say, we tried the 'external' treatment but, in the end, I was forced to reach for the rubber gloves. He wasn't best pleased at the prospect of an internal coccyx adjustment but very happy that, after two treatments, his bottom no longer hurt and he could get back to his animals. Definitely not placebo, I think.

One of the things that gives me most satisfaction is helping keep the cog wheels running for very elderly osteo-arthritic patients, allowing them better movement and improved circulation, in what I and the patients themselves have come to think of as a WD40 treatment. We don't pretend to have a cure for arthritis, but it is nice to be able to interrupt the daily grind of pain and stiffness with treatment and advice on management – often we 'home visit' and are able to assess their worst fears it situ.

Pain can be brought on by trauma. Trauma itself varies greatly, depending on the individual. I was once called out to the home of a dear elderly lady who was recovering from a bilateral (both) knee replacements (not great planning....). However, I had not been summoned to deal with her knees. On arrival, I learned that she had reacted badly to her medication and consequently suffered a vomiting attack. Unable to kneel over the toilet, she had been forced to bend from the waist, and had sent her lumbar spine into acute spasm.

It is astonishing how many of my patients, during the seven years in which I have been in practice, have had a similar experience whilst sat on the lav in the midst of a coughing or sneezing fit.

When I am on holiday, or out with groups of people I am not familiar with, and the conversation turns to work, I opt to have a career behind the checkout. It might kill the *craic* but it works for me.

I remember a coach trip with my mother, when the average age of the traveller was about

67. I was definitely on the *Tesco* payroll that week. Or so I thought...

On the final evening I found myself listening to a lady explaining how her 30-ish-year-old daughter had been 'under the hospital' for more than two years, in an as yet unsuccessful attempt to discover the cause of a pain she was experiencing in her upper right torso. She had apparently undergone scans, blood screening, ultrasound etc. etc., during in-patient and emergency admission, yet no-one appeared to be any the wiser. Sadly, my storyteller's other child had died, at the tender age of four, from liver failure and, naturally, everyone was drawing worrying conclusions, not least the patient herself.

Somewhat reluctantly, I eventually admitted to my real profession (I'm a sucker for enigmas), and asked her if anyone had looked at her daughter 'structurally'. She wasn't entirely certain what I meant by this, but said she would get her to phone me when we got back.

On my return, the phone duly rang and, after chatting with me briefly, the daughter made an appointment for that same week. No sooner was she standing in front of me than it was clear that her right leg was half an inch length shorter than the left. When she stood 'at rest', her spine made a 'c' shape (instead of a normal straight vertical 'I' shape), with the concavity of the 'c' on the right side. As a result, her anterior-lateral (front and side) ribs, diaphragm, liver, gall bladder etc. were all effectively being compressed.

I'm not sure what I had expected to find, but it wasn't that. I was relieved there were no obvious systemic causes - the liver is capable of creating symptoms anatomically 'miles' away. But leg length difference can often be the cause of postural 'compensation' and, a few treatments and a strategically-placed wedge in the heel of her shoe later, her pain had diminished greatly and her concern was largely allayed. This lady's case was highly unusual - I do think worry played a massive part in her condition, but her tissue presentation and pain were real enough.

I seldom employ the use of heel lifts with patients as they can often lead to problems elsewhere in the body, particularly in the knee and hip joints. However, I do advocate their use with children, as long as they are continually monitored. Last year, I assessed a two-year-old lad whose paramedic parents were very concerned because he kept complaining that his leg and, in particular, his knee, hurt. Having spent a considerable amount of time at hospital trying to establish why, his mother arranged for me to look at him structurally. What I discovered is that he had well over half an inch leg length difference. *"I wondered why none of his trousers seem to fit him properly and one side of them is always scuffed"*, his mum exclaimed. This little chap will almost certainly be benefiting from a heel raise.

My final tale of woe involved a young lady who managed to fall very badly on to her elbow whilst ice skating at the Eden Project. I didn't get to examine her until nine months after the fall and think I was a last resort. She was complaining of severe, continuous pain to the wrist, elbow and front shoulder. Her GP had seemingly arranged an X-ray, but had formed no conclusions based on the results. She had had continuous, private physiotherapy for nine months, but had felt no benefit and her medication had made no appreciable difference. She was also complaining of random coldness, numbness and *hyperasthesia* (pins and needles-esque) in the lower arm and hand.

After five vigorous treatments with me she had made no progress at all. I made contact with her GP, who decided to increase her medications and refer her to an orthopaedic consultant for assessment. This led to a referral with a neurologist for a nerve conduction test to determine which nerves, if any, were causing the pain. The results were negative and she was returned to the orthopaedic consultant. Throughout this time her symptoms were continuous and unrelenting. Five months after meeting her, I spoke with a neurologist about her symptoms and outcomes of investigations and he suggested that an MRI might provide some of the 'missing' information.

Unfortunately, it didn't - all results drew a blank. Then, some months later, I was attending a conference in London where a Consultant Vascular/General Surgeon was discussing a condition known as thoracic outlet syndrome – a rather complicated condition of the upper extremity. It was all starting to sound rather familiar to me, when, suddenly, the fire alarm sounded. We were asked to congregate in the car park where I found myself sidling up to him and explaining the now two-year-old problem my patient was facing. He asked me to refer the patient directly to him, with a copy of my findings, etc.

Some months later the patient underwent exploratory surgery with this surgeon, which turned into a rib section (part of her rib was removed). I was lucky enough to attend the procedure with this very enigmatic surgeon at the helm. I guessed immediately that he was highly respected and revered, simply because of the sheer numbers of students attending the surgery that day. He explained at the outset that, due to the lack of demonstrable evidence for a diagnosis, he would be undertaking an exploratory procedure and that he would act according to what was found once 'in'.

The story for this young lady did not end here unfortunately, as, some twelve months later she underwent further surgery to decompress a nerve at the elbow. It transpired that despite all the testing she had a double crush injury from the initial fall. However, her sense of humour prevailed throughout. After her initial rib-section she had vowed to make a feature of the removed rib – she was studying jewellery making at the time and we discussed the possibility of making a brooch.... I advised her that she would need to expose the bone to oxygen, which would allow the soft tissues to drop off, making it easier to clean. She responded that she would have to do so in the airing cupboard, or somewhere else out of the reach of her cat, who, clearly had his eye on it...

Chapter 8:   Part of the Establishment?

There will inevitably be changes within the health service over the next few years and these may lead eventually to professions such as mine entering the NHS on a contractual basis. In fact, if enough people demanded it, your surgery might consider looking into the provision of manual therapy (see Chapter 11 on the *National Institute for Clinical Excellence* report). However, as I have said, until our results are supported by a stronger evidence base, we will not be understood or endorsed as a profession by other healthcare providers.

The *Health and Social Care Act 2012* proposed the creation of clinical commissioning groups (CCGs), made up of general practitioners, who now oversee the planning and commissioning of health services. In the West Country we are establishing *Patient Participation Groups (PPGs)* which will include members of the public. They are designed to act as a streaming system between GPs and their patients and it is proposed they will become integral in the commissioning procedures. So, for those of you that wish to see osteopathy on the NHS, this will be your first point of contact.

I do see a manual therapy future in mainstream NHS as part of an integrated pain management approach, although it doesn't necessarily need to be called osteopathy, physiotherapy or chiropractic.

How would it work? As an NHS osteopath, I would probably be paid for an agreed number of sessions in which to improve the patient's condition. Unfortunately, of course, there are obvious reasons why it is not possible to predict the length of a treatment programme. A prolapsed disc and chronic arthritis are not comparable and neither is their recovery time. Moreover, individual patients cannot all be assumed to take the same length of time to respond.

There is also the issue of onus and responsibility. Although patient expectations vary, most do want to get better as soon as possible. But there are some who feel that it is the physician's or therapist's responsibility to 'heal' them and who are not prepared to play an 'active' part in their own recovery. Many NHS practitioners have been disillusioned by the experience of treating said patients. How many of you, as patients, have emerged from a ten-minute consultation with your GP, having been given valuable advice, that you then totally ignore, and/or a prescription that you promptly threw in the bin? Quite a few, I'll wager. What is the point? Some of the responsibility for recovery surely has to sit with the individual him or herself. But there is very little control of this waste of time and money.

Would I like to work within the NHS? Well, no.... not full-time, anyway. Not because I make a fortune working in the private sector: I do not. But I would find the waiting time that we all have to endure in the hands of the NHS rather challenging.

I know that this is largely unavoidable, that demand is high and resources are low. But, typically, during the three to six weeks a patient will roughly wait for an NHS appointment, the pain will have either: a) gone (in an ideal world); b) significantly worsened; or c) 'morphed' into a wider problem. At the same time, the patient's level of anxiety will probably also have risen, and with it their expectations.

However long the wait, whether for physio, x-ray, pain clinic or consultancy, the potential for other 'knock-on' physical and non-physical difficulties steps up apace. In times gone by, when employees were paid while on 'sick leave', there was not always, dare I say, quite the same urgency to have a 'problem' addressed. However, these days many of our patients not only arrive in pain but are visibly stressed at having to take time away from work. Employers are far less forgiving during this economic downturn, especially when the 'problem' doesn't have a big scar, abrasion or plaster cast as supporting evidence - and an individual's sickness record can leave a 'scar' on his or her cv. As for the self-employed, they are the ones who usually turn up after 6:30pm on a weekday, or on a Saturday morning. They simply cannot afford time off work. But the NHS makes little accommodation for them.

Frustratingly, the wider impact of waiting lists is largely ignored and unaccounted for. The cost of providing care or a care home when the family carer has gone sick is high, and the longer the wait for their treatment the higher the public services costs.

When a patient hands over a fee, no matter how great or small the sum, he or she tends to listen, and to value the advice, whether it is about exercise, diet, or whatever, and to spend the rest of their week complying with it, and altering their lifestyle to accommodate it.

This positive attitude has an impact on the patient's speed of recovery and leaves them wiser in the event of a return of the problem.

Patients are prepared to pay osteopaths, chiropractors and private physiotherapists because they want good advice and treatment. And they want time spent on them. If they have been listened to for 30 minutes, say, for which they have handed over hard cash, they are far more likely to follow advice and take the necessary action.

We, of course, are not alone in our 'privatisation'. There are many consultants of all types occupying roles as both public and private practitioner. And to Dr Benjamin Daniels, who claims we manual therapists are making money from people's ill fortune and who states that, as an NHS GP, his services are provided for free, I say, *"Nay, nay, I think not."* He receives an annual salary, siphoned from the taxation coffers to which we all contribute, and he will draw a handsome pension from the same source. As a private practitioner, I can only rely on my reputation and results for my living. Yes, he is more 'qualified' in medicine, but we have our own field of expertise and, as I have occasionally been told by surgeons, we provide a modest service in the front line that keeps patients out of their operating theatres. Although, there are one or two who clearly don't hold this view...

As a 'newbie' to the profession, set free to practice amongst the good people of the West Country, I was keen to become acquainted as early as possible with the local GP surgeries and relevant hospital consultants. I can say, wholeheartedly, that I was well received. But, there's always one exception, isn't there?

I shimmied down to a private hospital, keen to hear a talk being given by a consultant spinal surgeon, who, in my view, was clearly touting for private patients. He began presenting his slides, turning on the charm, and was in full flow until the moment his screen displayed what looked like a couple of Chinese or Japanese men pulling apart the body of a third man. Surprise, surprise, the caption read 'chiropractic and osteopathy'. He looked blankly at his audience, smiled broadly, shrugged his shoulders, and said, "Weeelllll, I don't really know what they do, so I guess I shouldn't say anything". Titter, titter....

I sat on my hands at the back of the room, seething. *"Don't put your hand up, DO*

NOT put your hand up", I implored myself. I remained admirably restrained, but drove home boiling with anger. Seriously, had it not occurred to him that, at some point in his career, a chiropractor or osteopath might actually cross his path? Surely it was his job to know, or at least have a fundamental grasp of, what they do? Or was it?

Whatever, I made it my mission to educate the poor misguided man...

I telephoned his office the next day but, by the time I finally got hold of him, he had been made fully aware that he was being hunted down by an aggravated osteopath who had attended his cattle market - I mean, spinal surgical procedures talk the night before. The element of surprise was lost. He was courteous and polite and when I gently tackled his disparagement of osteopathy, he replied,

"How do you propose to rectify this oversight"?

"Perhaps you might have a treatment", I suggested.

"How long will this take?" he replied.

"Less than an hour", was my answer. (I could almost physically hear his brain ticking over) *"How the hell do I get out of this one?"*

"Could I not just read a book?" he responded.

"Um, it took me five years to learn..." was my incredulous retort.

"No, I mean just the principles" (*"retreat, retreat"*, he's thinking.) *"I'll tell you what, we have a national conference coming up in May; how about you come along to that and speak"?*

(*"Ha!"* I could hear him thinking again, *"Get out of that one!"*)

"That would be great," I enthused, having no problem with large audiences and public speaking. *"You didn't see that one coming did you"*, I chuckled to myself later.

Somehow, he still managed to wriggle out of this offer. He later claimed that someone else had been organising the conference and he had passed my name on to them, but I heard no more. However, our 'relationship', such as it was, didn't end there. What this man failed to understand was that I was attempting to form alliances within the parallel medical professions (public and private), because I often need to make private referrals. He missed the point entirely.

In the following months and years I continued to attempt to gain his respect by sending private referrals. I was still quite new to the profession and didn't know any better, or anyone else.   For all I know I was helping to finance his private yacht in the Caribbean, yet, in his correspondence to me, he didn't even bother to acknowledge my title or that of my practice. I felt it was unprofessional and I got a bit disheartened. A year or so later I was at the hospital for a very different reason and thought I might pay a visit to his office. He wasn't there but, after speaking to a member of staff, I came to the conclusion that it wasn't a personal thing about me at all; he was just a pompous knob, who thought he was God and that the answer to everything was the knife, while everything else was just tosh.

Well what a relief that was.   You get people like this in every walk of life, of course, and we've all come across them. Suffice to say he was *the* worst I've yet to encounter, although his was a hard act to follow. Another member of the hospital staff gave me the names of some of his more amenable colleagues, and I now refer all my private and NHS work to them.

I'm not purposely grumbling about GPs, consultants or any other healthcare providers, but, really, the reason we are a rapidly growing profession is because we do get good results. We suffer because we haven't accrued enough satisfactory evidence which supports manual therapy claims. Patient testimonials, sadly, are not enough.

As GPs get younger (or maybe I'm just getting older...), their understanding of 'manual therapy' is increasing. They don't appreciate being kept out of the loop and, of course, it's better for the patient if they're not. Good communication saves expense and time (not to mention the odd life and limb) and I have focused hard on achieving this in my corner of the world, winning, I believe, considerable respect for it. Colleagues elsewhere have not been embraced so favourably, which is a big concern when they are faced with very sick mutual patients.

Very early in my career, I was faced with an active elderly patient whom I suspected had either a vertebral wedge fracture (often spontaneous cracks in the vertebra) or a myeloma (bone cancer). I relayed my concerns in a letter to the patient's GP but the letter does not appear to have been followed up. In hindsight, I still feel I should have done more in this situation, making telephone contact and perhaps being more insistent but, at the time, I didn't think it was my place *to* insist. Had I done so, his myeloma (for that's what it was), may have been diagnosed and treated sooner. I strongly felt the onus was mine and that I could have done more and thereupon made changes to the way I communicate to the wider healthcare providers.

In another recent encounter, a GP outside my catchment was most aggrieved that I had discussed with a mutual patient the possible cause of her pain, declaring: *"I don't like patients to have preconceived ideas of what is wrong with them"*. I found this astounding and, quite honestly, utter nonsense. When faced with a 44-year-old underweight female with back pain and history of an early hysterectomy, it surely would be prudent to suggest a bone density scan so as to rule out early osteoporosis? These attitudes are far and few, but they do need to change. In this instance, the GP had never even met the patient; I, on the other hand, had spent three separate sessions examining and treating her – is there room for this kind of complacency in healthcare?

Chapter 9: What's the difference?

If I had a pound for every time someone asked me *"what's the difference between a chiropractor and an osteopath?"* I would be a wealthy woman. The standing joke among osteopaths is *"about 30k a year"*. The real answer, though, is *"not much"*. We have minor differences in principle, but, in my opinion many of these date back to views held by the founders of the professions (Mr Palmer and Mr Still). We have an equal knowledge of human anatomy etc... Chiropractors are also trained in the use of x-rays, but they are not radiographers in the true sense - radiography has many more facets to its title than x-ray alone.

To the patient, and in practice, we differ only in the delivery of our techniques. One particularly marked variation is in the delivery of high velocity thrusts (HVTs), short, sharp adjustments to joints – read more on this in chapter 11). In treating the neck, osteopaths learn to deliver this thrust 'in flexion' (chin tucked into chest), whereas chiropractors are mostly taught to deliver 'in extension' (head tilted backwards). For safety's sake, I would choose the former, simply because the vertebral artery (which passes through the upper lateral part of the neck) is not under as much tension (or pulling force) in flexion. In reality, I don't use either of them.

Most manual therapists – osteopaths, chiropractors and physiotherapists - are hard-working, honest and diligent. But there will always be exceptions. Just as in other professions, we have our 'poor performers'. As I have continued to urge, do your research before you book the appointment; if they sound too good to be true, they probably are.

Some chiropractors, and possibly few osteopaths and physiotherapists, too, are reputed to encourage patients to sign up for a 'course of treatments'? I don't know whether this is true, but it's what some patients have told me in the past. And, of course, it is wrong. Patients will often only need one or two treatments. So, question whether you are getting better after two or three treatments and, if not, ask your practitioner why they think this is.

What are Cranial Osteopathy and Cranio-sacral Therapy?

I've also often been asked about the differences between Cranial Osteopathy [CO] and Cranio-sacral Therapy [CST]. The short answer is that COs are osteopaths, CSTs are not.

Both methods of treating the body through a 'hands-on', but non-invasive, touching approach, usually involving the practitioner putting his or her hands on the cranium and, sometimes, other parts of the body. They both 'claim' to treat musculoskeletal conditions, as well as other illnesses.

Cranial osteopaths have a much broader range of bio-mechanical and systemic knowledge than cranio-sacral therapists, although much of the theory and the techniques are similar. After attaining a BSc (Hons) in osteopathy, they (cranial osteopaths) move on to a post-graduate course specialising in cranial work. However, they are not 'formally' regulated; CO is not recognised by the GOsC, and you will not find cranial osteopaths on its website search facility, because the GOsC does not endorse cranial osteopathy.

Whilst the jury is still out on the question of its efficacy, it does have a large and faithful following and is a popular treatment of choice for parents of babies and young children. As for evidence based research, frankly, there is very little and what does exist is very poor.

Cranio-sacral therapists train for two years, at the end of which they receive a diploma. Although they normally register with the *Cranio-sacral Therapy Association*, they are not currently regulated. Plans for voluntary regulation under the auspices of the *Complementary and Natural Healthcare Council (CNHC)*, were shelved in 2011 when the Council's funding was pulled by *The Prince's Foundation for Integrated Health* and the *Department of Health*.

A 2004 blog on *'The Guardian'* website by the *'Bad Science'* founder, Dr Goldacre, posed the question, *"Where is the evidence?"* He was inviting all cranio-sacral therapists and cranial osteopaths to point him in the direction of the research.   Unsurprisingly, perhaps, no compelling conclusions have been forwarded...

'Cranial' websites meanwhile appear to get round any advertising restrictions simply by advising patients to phone the practitioner to 'chat' about their ailment – in this way, they aren't promoting any specific treatment claims at all.

The concern of many mainstream osteopaths, who are busy fighting their own evidence based battle, is that their case may be damaged by association with 'cranial' osteopaths. Opinion is divided, but there is a feeling that cranial osteopaths dilute the credibility of the profession because cranial work fails to provide any evidence *at all* that it works.

While it informs its followers about what they call the 'cranial rhythm', it has yet to provide proof of its existence, let alone that it can be 'adjusted', as is claimed. Cranial osteopaths argue that mainstream osteopaths are simply incapable of sensing the more subtle palpations that they claim to experience..... and therefore mainstream osteopathy's armoury is lacking a valuable, non-invasive treatment.

You have probably gained the impression that I'm not a fan. Well, I'm not really. I am a scientist and I believe that science provides us with platforms to prove and disprove our theories. We have to temporarily suspend belief in the unattested. CST/CO may indeed be one of those discoveries of the future, but until a new evidence breakthrough, it has to follow the same qualifying procedures.

Having said all of that...... I received a course of CST about ten years ago which saved my sanity, and it pains me that I cannot scientifically explain 'how'.

I didn't know anything of CST as a first year student and spent a huge amount of my time following osteopaths and cranial therapists around - work shadowing to glean knowledge. While doing so, I met a CST practitioner who became a friend. A year or so later, I found myself under an immense amount of stress and began to suffer from anxiety attacks and hyperventilation. These gradually worsened and were starting to take over my life. Faced with a prescription for beta-blockers, I pitched up at my friend's for help. After maybe eight sessions, for which he made no charge because I was a student, I was cured. At least, I have never suffered an attack since.

I have to say that I believe my successful treatment was purely down to the extra-ordinary power of placebo, which feels slightly mean and will affront many. All the same, I offer the following, from www.cranial.org/uk, the website of the *William Sutherland School* (it's a members' register, not a regulator).

"Cranial osteopathy is a refined and subtle type of osteopathic treatment that encourages the release of stresses and tensions throughout the body, including the head. It is a gentle yet extremely effective approach and may be used in a wide range of conditions for people of all ages, from birth to old age.

"Osteopaths may have different specialities including sports injuries, paediatrics, and visceral osteopathy (treating the internal organs of the body). Cranial osteopathy embraces all of these".

Involuntary Motion- The Cranial Rhythm

"Cranial osteopaths are trained to feel a very subtle, rhythmical shape change that is present in all body tissues. Known as Involuntary Motion or the Cranial Rhythm, this was first described in the early 1900s by Dr. William G. Sutherland and its existence was confirmed in a series of laboratory tests in the 1960's and '70's. Since the movement is of very small amplitude,

it takes practitioners with a very finely developed sense of touch to feel it."

Dr Sutherland suggested that the bones of the cranium can actually move. In his book *'With Thinking Fingers'*, he suggests that, as a result, they can even be 'adjusted' and, therefore, 'corrected'. Cranial osteopaths and cranio-sacral therapists believe that the bones of a cadaver won't move because no fluid is being pumped around them – that it is the presence of fluid in a live patient that allows adjustment to be made. This flies in the face of current science, which has observed from *post mortem* surgery that, by the time we reach adulthood, the cranium has fused into one solid bone.

During our training we were given an option to study cranial osteopathy during clinic hours. We had the chance to practise it and discuss our findings with the 'cranial clinician'. In truth, the only thing I could feel was skin, bony prominences - and a pulse if I happened to be near to an artery. I had never really been convinced of its efficacy in the first place, and became disillusioned quite quickly. So I gave up and decided I would be going down the bio-mechanical avenue, which, to be truthful, suited my need to know the *'whats'* and *'whys'* perfectly.

Whenever cranio-sacral therapists and cranial osteopaths have subsequently tried to explain the technicalities of what they are 'doing', I have not come close to comprehending. In my view, this lack of understanding tends to create a 'them and us' situation between practitioner and patient, where the practitioner is saying, *"we are the experts, you just be grateful for the treatment"*. But, in my experience, you have to be able to relate to your patients, to explain what you are doing, and why. I have a good level of medical training and yet I am still left completely dumbfounded by some of the treatment explanations I have been given by individuals of this profession.

Chapter 10: Down to Your Underwear, Please

We see all shapes and sizes, day in day out, and, believe me, you begin to regard the human body entirely differently when you see eight of them a day. I appreciate that some people are a little uncomfortable in their skins, but it's really what your body and its joints can and cannot do that we are interested in, and in order to look at those mechanics, you need to be undressed.

It is not always necessary for you to strip off, but you should expect to do so at least on your first few visits. We're looking for tissue tension, asymmetry and restrictions etc., and frankly, we can't see these if you've got your clothes on. Once we have an idea of how your body works and copes with our treatment, it becomes a little easier to negotiate clothing. But you wouldn't expect to go and see at dentist and not open your mouth, would you?

Seriously, one of my clinicians told us a scary story (maybe he just made it up, who knows?), about his training days as a physiotherapist, when a friend 'popped in for a popping' as you might say. He laid him prone on the treatment table, fully clothed, and commenced with what we call the butterfly technique; well, this chap turned out to have a boil on his back, which, yes, you guessed it, duly popped. He bled all over the place – his shirt, the table, the carpet... The moral of the story? Always examine your patients undressed.

However ..... I also distinctly remember another lecturer telling us that it was "not appropriate" to comment on things like underwear, fashion and suchlike. And, all in all, I can honestly say I have never done that – despite intense provocation (I am eternally perplexed by 'lunch box' and similarly labelled underwear). But it cuts both ways, surely? If you know you have an appointment with an osteopath, chiropractor or physio, it's fairly likely, isn't it, that you will have a modicum of undressing to do; so why, oh why, don your g-string thong, your loose pair of boxer shorts or the tightest , hole-iest, dirtiest or most inappropriate underwear?

You are not preparing for a massage. You will need to move around the couch quite consistently, and often be asked to take up precarious-looking positions. Think of it as the equivalent of a game of 'Twister' on a treatment couch. Is a strapless bra or 'form-hugging' briefs the garment of choice? No.

The male patient with loose boxer shorts is another example of our exasperation when trying to get on and treat you: it is nigh on impossible to treat a chap whose plums are helplessly making an appearance every time you move him and he knows it. Hamstring stretches are virtually unachievable while the patient is imitating a star fish. *"Good towelling"*, I hear one clinician wailing at me.... *"Decent underwear"*, I wail back.

Some of you have no problems at all with taking off your clothes in front of us. Indeed, many years ago, one such patient, who used to appear in Cornwall every so often to help out with a very famous garden, had no problems at all with his nudity. He proceeded to strip naked each time he arrived for a treatment, asking, *"Where do you want me?"* Now, where did I put that reflex hammer.....?

Then there was the very elderly gentleman who asked if I could treat him in his own home as he could no longer drive. He and his even older and similarly immobile, but new, wife greeted me with all the civilities and gratitude that patients do when I have travelled a fair distance. I duly commenced with history-taking etc. and set up my mobile treatment bench in their rather cramped living room. He then undressed, and, although I obviously averted my eyes during his disrobing, he finally stood there in a full set of frilly pants, suspenders and stockings. Not a single word passed my lips as, thankfully, he changed into some shorts. Having examined him, I eventually began treatment for what were very arthritic knees, but was having difficulty finding room to manoeuvre, until I noticed a door to a conservatory that appeared to be virtually empty. *"That would have been an ideal place to set up the treatment table"*, I thought. It was then that I spotted an airer in the corner of the room, sagging under the weight of a mountain of basques, suspenders, stockings and crotch-less panties. I did return to finish his course of treatment, but promised myself that, if he once mentioned his choice of underwear, it would almost definitely be the last time his knees were in my hands.

Another of my male patients once 'forgot' to remove his pink bra. He was quite opinionated with regards to women and felt that they should only be wearing skirts – no matter what their profession... His face was also quite a pretty pink as soon as he realized his *faux pas* and he did not mention clothing ever again.

As my lecturer maintained, we're not here to judge (not in respect of undies at least) ... but neither do we necessarily want to witness patients' idiosyncrasies.

Which leads me next on to the very delicate matter of hygiene. My daughter once said to me that she couldn't do my job as it often required the handling of sweaty, unwashed bodies, and, more to her point, feet.

The fact is that a person's odour can be quite telling (and not just that they have forgotten where they've put the soap). And, to be honest, smelly feet and bodies don't really bother me. On only one occasion, when confronted with vinegary smelling feet, did my stomach lurch. However, one particular patient broke all 'olfactory' boundaries by reminding me, almost proudly, every time he visited me that, due to age and arthritis, he was no longer able to wipe his bum.

Chapter 11:   Let's Get to the Crunch and be 'NICE' about it

Let's be honest, *'bone-crunching'* is what, however unfairly, we osteopaths, chiropractors and even some physiotherapists are best known for.   Otherwise known as 'wiggly clicks', 'manipulation', 'bone popping', 'cracking', and yes, osteopaths even refer to thoracic HVT as 'dogging'..... In more ways than one, I find this unfortunate.

High Velocity, Low Amplitude thrusts (HVLA), the technical term for said 'bone-crunching', is to put it at its simplest, a form of musculo-skeletal re-alignment. It is also known commonly as HVT (High Velocity Thrusting), joint mobilisation, spinal manipulation therapy... among many other things. It is used primarily on the spine and pelvis, although, if you're very unfortunate, you may have other areas of your body manipulated. Yet, as the saying goes, *"A monkey could do it"*. There is any number of courses out there. Some promise the ability to execute the technique in as little as two days, would you believe?

But let me say straight away that we don't all 'crack' or 'pop' bones. Among those who do, some are much better, than others; but many of us don't really see its necessity at all. Or, come to that, its future. And yet.... almost all osteopathic and chiropractic research up to now, at least 80% - has focussed on the application and efficacy of HVLA/HVT.

As a practitioner who doesn't even use HVLA, I find this particularly frustrating. I understand that there are many chiropractors, physiotherapists and osteopaths who seem happy enough to confine themselves to HVLA/HVT thrusts – one reason why research focuses almost exclusively on it, I imagine – but, as I have continued to stress, there are more techniques in existence than this. And, I fear, we are failing to explore the wider potential of other techniques being utilised.

As one of my clinicians used to say at University, if the only thing you have in your tool bag is a hammer then everything tends to look like a nail... And that is my biggest issue with this technique. It is impressive, it *does* require a high level of training and knowledge to execute effectively and efficiently, but in my view, it is too commonly used. (I hear applause and booing at the same time, I wonder which is the louder...)

So what exactly is an HLVA/HVT technique, and how, why and when is it used? And perhaps more importantly, does it work at all? Well, read on and judge for yourself.

HLVA and HVT are hardly new concepts and instances of bone-setting feature in historical records around the world. The Romans and Greeks termed those executing and practising bone-setting as 'skeleton men', while the ancient Egyptians simply called them 'men of the hands'. The Chinese and others even extended the practice into the setting of fractures and joint dislocations; they and other cultures still use these procedures today as a cheaper, and 'better understood', option than the surgical procedures we have adopted in the West.

It was these ancestors of ours who first developed the great palpatory skills required to feel the muscles, joints or other soft tissues that we manual therapists use today.

The facet joints or *zygoapophyseal joints* are located at the back of the spine helping to provide movement in each individual segment (spinal bone) of the spine. They work 'in collaboration' with the front half of the spine, where the discs and the big vertebral wedges are found. Occasionally, the facet joints or the tissues surrounding them can become inflamed and go into spasm, which will generally slow down movement in the spine, in an attempt to prevent further damage occurring. However, the facet joints can occasionally become, for want of a better phrase, 'stuck together', like chewing gum stuck to your shoe, and reduce the rather elegant individual spinal movement still further – and that's when the pain kicks in.

There is a multitude of possible physical reasons for this, but it would not be useful to explore them here; some patients might only ever experience this 'facet lock' or 'facet irritation', once, but others may endure many years of episodic re-occurrence. Some eventually need to resort to injection therapy techniques as an outpatient and a few are forced to undergo a *'facetectomy'*, whereby a small piece of bone is removed, thus decompressing this joint and the nerves feeding it.

Bear in mind facet irritation is not the only example of why we might employ HVLA/HVT techniques, although it is a common one. From a 'general' osteopathic point of view, however, the execution of an HVLA/HVT would be the choice of treatment if a patient were presenting with a facet joint 'lock'.

So what does happen when one undergoes HVLA/HVT? Onomatopoeic terms like 'crunching' and 'popping' describe the sound you'll probably hear during the procedure. Physiologically, the actual 'popping' sound is believed to be caused by an event known as 'cavitation', which occurs within the synovial fluid of this *diarthrodial* joint. The relief gained by patients is described as a neuro-physiological effect, as the thrust creates a state of *'hypoalgesia'*, or less pain, in the segment/level of spine being thrust.

The 'HV' or 'high velocity' force with which the thrust is delivered separates two or more of these facet joints, and 'releases' the tissues surrounding them. Applying the right amount of pressure to the spine is part of the skill of the practitioner.

And, just in case you're wondering, yes, there are '*low* velocity thrust' varieties as well. LVIs require the patient to adopt the same position as they would for an HVLA/HVT, but they utilise the patients' deep breathing to expand the diaphragm and some parts of the spine and the practitioner will gently encourage the tissues to stretch. My view is that the tissues have already reached the maximum stretch using this adaptation, so why force them beyond it with high velocity force? Yes, yes, I've heard all the arguments, it is just my opinion.

Some patients express disappointment at not getting a 'pop'; and they do ask... I have a well used analogy for them. I get them to imagine the bones of the human body as a puppet. The puppets strings however, represent human muscles and tendons. As an osteopath I tend to work on these structures more often than not - (strings – or muscles and tendons – better known as soft tissues). I believe this gives the joints of the body optimal space to work and do their 'thing' It is my thought that manual therapists using HVLA/HVT in isolation are only treating the 'body' of the puppet (or human joints) and not so much its strings which are the leverage systems of joints. There are some manual therapists who do use this technique almost exclusively and I'm not convinced that is what manual therapy is about.

It was a neurophysiologist, Dr Irvin Korr, known to his friends as Kim, and his colleagues, who, during the 1950s, developed and published the theory of 'facilitated segments'. In lay terms, he established that each segment or level of the spinal cord (e.g. *L5* or *C2*) is responsible for organizing 'segmented' disease processes.

From this, he theorised that each nerve which exits its spinal segment or level follows a pathway and that this pathway ultimately stops at one or more junctions to perform 'tasks', such as pumping the muscles of your heart, helping you reach for the coffee jar or just registering pain.   It then stops and relays information back to the brain, which then decides whether or not to act. Remember Descartes' image illustration of the pain pathway? His *'Traite de l'homme'* - 'my foot is burning in the fire, therefore I need to remove it from the flames'?   Korr surmised that, if the spinal segment or level was spasming or dysfunctional, its associated pathways might also be affected.

Dr. Korr theorised that HVLA/HVT could help to relieve spasm or tissue tension, allowing the spinal segment (joint) and its nerve pathways to function correctly again. For the first time in its history, research appeared to be backing one of osteopathy's principal techniques – the licence to crack.

To some people this piece of research seems to be incomplete. It was postulated that if, as in the case of an HVLA/HVT executed at, for example, the upper lumbar spine (L1/2/3) to alleviate 'segmental' pain, the practitioner might, depending on what was causing the obstruction, achieve a good outcome and rid the patient of the pain in both that joint and in its associated nerve pathways. This theory was then applied to other structures within the body such as the heart and lungs (which have some of their functions exiting from the upper part of the thoracic spine). The question arose, if it can work with some pathways (i.e. the spinal segments), why not all of the associated pathways? The question has never really been answered.

Then, in 2000, Prof Eyal Lederman, Director for the Centre for Professional Development in Osteopathy and Manual Therapy (CPDO), claimed to have found evidence of neuro-physiological flaws in Dr Korr's 'facilitated segments' theory. Even more importantly, though, he pointed out that no-one had taken the research further, to assess the efficacy of HVLA – or indeed, *any other manual techniques/clinical applications.*

As I have been saying, there was a dearth of evidence available regarding this and other manual therapy techniques and, to my mind, there still is. Why is this? After all, medicine spends a vast amount of time, energy and money, quite rightly, on finding the right drugs or surgical procedures to fix our aches and pains. Pain trials take place by the thousand.

To be fair, manual therapy conducts its trials too – but, as we have seen, the results do not represent a true reflection of 'manual therapy techniques' because those trials focus almost exclusively on spinal joint mobilisation/HVT.

Let me explain. In a real life manual therapy situation, any patient entering a clinic, whatever their age, race, sex, occupation etc., would be physically assessed by an expert, then treated accordingly with whichever of a number of techniques the practitioner deemed most appropriate in his or her clinical judgement and experience (as well, of course, as being offered practical 'do's and don'ts' advice, and maybe provided with exercises and/or postural advice).

What would *not* happen is what invariably takes place in most manual therapy research trials, where, whatever the initial examination and assessment show, (if there was one in the first place), the patient will be given a spinal adjustment (HVLA/HVT) or two, told to come back again a week or two later to be 'assessed' again — and then given exactly the same treatment as before. (Bear in mind, too, that musculoskeletal trials don't, for example, take into account that one of your participants may be a rugby player and another a dinner lady.)

So, the implication is that if spinal joint mobilisation works, good — if it doesn't, then osteopathy and other manual therapies using it have failed. Consequently, of course, the trials tend to produce mediocre results. Is it any wonder? Let's face it, manual therapy works precisely because we *don't* run our clinics as we run our trials.

In 2009, a government recommendation paper was published to help GPs and clinicians confronted with back pain. Entitled *'Low Back Pain — Early management of persistent non-specific low back pain'*, it was researched and written by the *National Institute for Clinical Excellence (NICE)*. Broad though its apparent terms of reference appeared to be, it did identify certain conditions to which it was not alluding, among them malignancy, *ankylosing spondylitis* (a chronic inflammatory disease) and other inflammatory disorders, fractures and infection.

All manual therapists, including massage therapists, emerged from this report smelling of roses, and were quite pleased with themselves. However, in my view, the paper was flawed. Its main aim was to provide best *cost effective* clinical guidance for the management of low back pain. At this point they could have all just packed up early and gone home, saving the public thousands of pounds, because the cheapest option is always medication and used almost exclusively by GPs as a first line of defence.

Its early management strategy advised *against* x-ray, MRI, injection therapy treatment, laser therapy, interferential, ultrasound, TENS machine use, lumbar support, traction, denervation and other electrotherapy alternatives – as you can see, it was already distancing itself from the idea of 'integrated back care' and edging its way towards the only six options left in terms of treatment; manual therapy, structured exercise, physical treatment, acupuncture, prescription therapy and psychological treatment.

A combination of these is exactly what it did call for. Along with drug treatment, it advocated one of the following: a structured exercise programme (12 weeks, 8 sessions); physical and/or psychological treatment (100 hours over 8 weeks); manual therapy (12 weeks, 9 sessions) or acupuncture (12 weeks, 10 sessions). But most manual therapists will tell you that pain doesn't necessarily 'go away' in a 12-week period. And the inclusion of medication always raises the question as to whether any success is due to the drugs or the therapy. Except, of course, when you are confronted with a patient who has been prescribed a series of anti-inflammatory drugs for fifteen plus years

The team that compiled these guidelines, including the Chair, Dr Martin Underwood (Professor of Primary Care Research) and Clinical Advisor Paul Watson (Professor of Pain Management and Rehabilitation), were specialists in the 'interventions' they were recommending. (Mr Watson's views were called to question by the *Pain Society* after he requested a withdrawal of the NICE guidelines shortly after they were published. Although they had been "based on the best possible research evidence and expert consensus", in reality, there was *no* appreciable representation of pain services on the panel. If a means of pain service provision is being called into question, surely the service deserves to be adequately represented by an expert in that field, and *all* the relevant research made available. Sadly, it is hard to resist the thought that the research was hand-picked to suit the panel's own beliefs.

One trial which appeared to have a significant influence on the panel was the *'UK BEAM Trial', Underwood et al BMJ 2004*. But wait a second, Underwood et al? Could this be the same Dr Martin Underwood, Chair of the NICE Guidelines for Low Back Pain 2009? You bet, it is. Come on, is this a healthy way to determine our service guidelines?

The UK BEAM Trial looked at cost effectiveness of physical exercise and spinal manipulation for back pain in primary care and private health services. Using a disability questionnaire, Roland Morris (see more on pain questionnaires – chapter 16) it set out to establish which benefited patients most; best care (usual GP back pain measures); best care plus exercise; best care plus manipulation (there's that bloody word again); or best care plus manipulation and exercise over three and twelve months. 'Manipulated' patients were given up to eight 20-minute sessions over twelve weeks, which included at least one HVLA/HVT.

Selection for the trial was based on the results of a questionnaire. Physical assessment does not appear to have been part of the criteria, aside to ascertain that their pain was between the bottom rib and gluteal folds (bottom of the bottom) and neither was occupation. This is utterly meaningless. It is not a comparison of any sort because the patients were not properly assessed or diagnosed, and neither were they anywhere close to being heterogeneous. Final outcomes were based on the results of the Roland Morris questionnaire. Trial results were 'low to moderate'. Surprise, surprise. Yet this research was used to assist or influence the NICE outcomes?

NICE also concluded that facet joint (spinal) injection therapies and denervations were also of little value. It claimed that the evidence was not there to support its use. No evidence? Clinic numbers continue to grow in Europe and America as we speak, with increasingly positive results. Why was this evidence ignored?

HVLA/HVT Close Encounters

Whether we have gone on to use them or not, we have all been taught how to execute various HVLA/HVT techniques. Our training mainly involved practising on each other for two or three years, before working as students in clinical practice, where patients were a mix of self-referrals and GP referral whose fees were reduced to reflect our student status. We did not move on to the paying public until reaching post-graduate status. We were guided through each stage by a skilled clinician and, on the whole, my experience, both at university and in the clinical teaching environment, was very structured.

However, in Years 4 and 5, we attended small clinical tutorials where the teaching environment could be a little less structured. There were one or two students, and even clinicians, who regarded HVLA/HVT as *'the'* treatment of choice and could be occasionally quite heavy-handed. I was left feeling winded and bruised, not to say pissed off - on more than one occasion. Long before I completed my training, I had begun to question the authenticity of this 'thrust until it pops' approach, and not long after qualifying I decided that HVLA/HVT was not for me.

Soon after I qualified, I did a six week locum 'favour' for a nearby, very experienced osteopath who was going on holiday. This osteopath had a fantastic following. However, I was quite surprised to discover how much HVLA/HVT was being persistently used on patients. Week after week, month after month, there seemed to be no variation at all and, if there was, it did not appear in patient notes.

One elderly gentleman had been receiving upper cervical spine manipulations for over 40 years although he had not begun treatment at this particular clinic until he was in his late 70s. Seemingly, he still 'depended' upon mobilisation treatments in order to achieve a normal-ish range of movement in his neck and a reduction in pain. Needless to say, I was unhappy, that, at his age, he was still having fortnightly HVLA/HVT.

I explained my concerns to him and outlined the possible implications of the treatment he was receiving and, for months afterwards, he came to me for soft tissue work on his neck. However, after two months, he confessed that he had returned to the 'manipulator' and, although he was now only having one 'pop' per month and coming to me once a month for soft tissue work, I was still quite deflated. But he was an educated man, who had weighed up the risks and decided that this treatment suited and worked for him. As a newly qualified osteopath who had chosen not to manipulate bones, that was a lesson.

I clearly remember, during my second year in clinic, meeting a young man who had been recently diagnosed with *ankylosing spondylitis*, a progressive disease that, over a period of years, can cause the pelvis, spine and ribs to fuse. This chap came to our clinic purely and simply for spinal mobilisation in the form of HVLA/HVT and, in his words, it was 'the only thing which gives me the freedom of movement I need to work and bring home a pay cheque'. I can still hear him saying that his consultant rheumatologist thought he should not be undergoing HVLA. There are many very valid reasons why – the danger of fracture later in life, for one – but what would you do in his place if conventional medicine was not providing any answers to medical and consequential financial problems?

Finally on this subject, it is a fact that patients don't always remember to tell you everything. You've been through their case history, past medical problems, you've examined them physically, you think you've been thorough, and then, halfway through the treatment, they blurt out that they had brain surgery ten years ago... (This has happened to me twice!) Or *"I did have a TIA (stroke) last year – but it wasn't serious, I'm fine now"*.... I'd prefer to err on the side of caution and not subject *any* patient to the kind of force delivered via HVT.

Which brings us to the question: Just how safe is HVLA/HVT? There is certainly evidence to suggest that HVLA/HVT can be harmful when applied to the upper cervical spine (neck). The *Journal of Neurology, Neurosurgery and Psychiatry (JNNP)* website lists hundreds of examples of damage ostensibly 'caused' by cervical spine manipulation, ranging from disc herniation to full disc protrusion into the spinal cord, causing massive complications, including paralysis and even death. Many of these cases are specifically related to vascular tears and *avulsions*, due to the close proximity of the vertebral and basilar arteries. However, given the scale of HVLA/HVT use, fatal incidents are rare. Certainly a whole lot rarer than accidental deaths and disability caused by more orthodox medical treatments, I would suggest.

Interestingly, the JNNP also highlights cases where patients have suffered an injury to this area by simply sneezing or moving into a yoga position. Indeed, I've often thought that a very interesting paper might be written on the rate of stroke occurrence among over-60s who have sat at the hairdressers with head held back in extension for ten minutes whilst having their hair washed in an ill-designed basin...

The possibility of micro-trauma arising as a result of a spinal manipulation is a concern. Repeated often enough, you have, in theory, the recipe for a list of undesirable conditions, among them accelerated osteo-arthritis and tissue hyper-mobility (leading to too much movement of the surrounding joints). Although this theory is far from proven, we know that tissues are quite predictable particularly as we age and more so in response to repetitive movement. We know that, as we get older, our tissues lose the ability to re-gain shape and adapt to rapid body movement as well as they do in our teens and early twenties. They tend to become 'more lax'. Why then would you want to regularly exert forces on joint tissues which stretch them further still?

At the end of the day, spinal mobilisation evidently brings temporary relief to many people even if it doesn't always have a lasting impact. The view of the *Cochrane Library*, the established database for all medical trials (see appendix), is that, while in the short term spinal mobilisation *may* be effective, there is little evidence that spinal

manipulation therapy is *superior* to other standard treatments. Now, I'm not

sure that any 'spinal mobilisers' are claiming to be superior in any way – but you can see that the problem is that there is a huge void where *all* manual therapy research should be.

Our credentials as osteopaths appear to rest on something which *might* work and which, even if it does, may be no better than anything else out there. We urgently need to represent manual therapy differently. Yet the patients keep coming...

It's my view that an integrated approach to back/joint pain is vital for the *early* management of patients. This means pharmacology, injection therapy, manual therapy, surgery, acupuncture and electrotherapy. Sometimes the integrated approach reaches into maternity care, social care, specialist oncology care and so on. It also means picking up the phone and talking to related department and health care providers, rather than relying on the impersonal 'advantages' of the computer.

Somewhat paradoxically, perhaps, we need more autonomy to achieve this. My working life involves frequent phone calls to varying departments of health and social care on behalf of my patients to press for this follow-up or that intervention. Alas, it seems the information mainly flows one way and it is rare that I am kept in the 'loop' unless the patient is a private referral. This is not progression.

As always, it comes down to money. We simply cannot afford an integrated system. Medicine will always be the cheaper option. The July 2012 review of the NICE report highlighted a number of concerns, chiefly "with implementation of the guideline (e.g. patients are not getting access to manual therapy and acupuncture". So, this very costly exercise seems to have done little to alter what patients are being offered in lower back pain management.

Today, I am often recommended by patients precisely because I *don't* perform HVLA/HVT. In all honesty, I have only needed to carry out this technique once or twice in my career and then only in the far less controversial lumbar spine area, choosing, some might argue the lengthier – but just as successful – treatments.

Chapter 12   *Is* There a Typical Patient?

The answer to that of course is 'no', there are no typical patients – you'd expect me to say that, but it's true. Patients come in all shapes, sizes, aches and pains. As you will read people present with a range of ailments that are perceived differently per individual whether caused either by work, exercise or just plain idiocy….

Occupational Hazards

One of the first questions we put to new patients is *"What do you do for a living?"* It's important, because certain occupations are obviously more prone to spinal and joint injury. The obvious, of course, are builders and labourers. It's more than normal wear and tear; there are the adverse weather conditions in which they often have to operate, not to mention their seemingly endless love for a cuppa and the toll this may take on their general well-being.

But there are also dentists with neck and back complaints from leaning over all day; bike riders whose heavy helmets turning up in clinic with neck pain; avid cyclists, on their way to and from work, often crashing into something, sliding along the ground, poorly galvanised with a road rash story or two to tell; long haul lorry drivers presenting with tight hip flexor muscles/ligaments and associated lower back pain due to sitting down all day; desk workers glued to the computer screen developing neck and wrist strain. I even had a seasonal ice-cream scooper with repetitive strain.

The over-zealous

We are often confronted with the *"I've swallowed a medical dictionary"* type, who proceeds to self-diagnose, throwing in the odd anatomical phrase or two as if to establish some kind of credentials. This can get a trifle annoying. To hear a patient say that they were told by a crystal therapist twelve years previously that their back was *"not in alignment"* means sweet FA to me. Likewise, another patient presenting with an 'assumed' disc problem diagnosed by a neighbour, *"because that's what happened to them"*, matters not a jot. But button my lip, I must.

Some patients come to me oozing with knowledge and enthusiasm about their bodily anomalies and what they are doing to keep things 'ticking over'. They are proud of the fact that they put time and effort into their day to optimise body function.

One such patient, at his first appointment, informed me that, as he had quite a sedate job, he cycled to work every day, as well as for pleasure at the weekends, ate a very healthy diet and used various gadgets to 'self massage', bathe his feet, etc. I noticed, however, that his eyes were significantly red and he told me that he had glaucoma.

When I dug a little deeper (and this took some weeks), it transpired that he was using an inversion table* - for 20 minutes every day. Needless to say, we had a long chat...

---

*For the uninitiated, an inversion table is a piece of equipment that enables you literally to hang upside down, an exercise whose purpose is to create traction in the spine. However, it will, of course, cause blood to gravitate to the head. Glaucoma is a condition which already has raised blood (intraocular) pressure behind the eyes. I would have hoped this might be mentioned in the small print of such a device, I have never checked...

Soon after the *Wii* was first marketed the term '*Wii* strain' was coined – the name given to the injuries suffered by those using it. I've had one or two Wii enthusiasts myself, but there are some corkers on the internet, where you can find various websites dedicated to the cuts and bruises attributed to the Wii, where the maimed proudly show off *You-tube* clips and photographs of their bad luck and misfortune.

I have yet to encounter a *'gangnam style'* or *'harlem shake'* injury, but I'm sure it's only a matter of time...

As for conversation during a treatment, I have been expected to take part in discussions on racism, fascism, pescatarianism, ageism, sexism, homophobia, domestic abuse, prison conditions, cleptomania, pyromania, addiction, farming, tourism and, of course, pasty taxes.

When booking an initial appointment, I prefer patients to make their own arrangements, (although I do appreciate the frustration that can be felt when a husband, wife, partner etc is in pain). This is not just so that I can establish some basics, but because I want to ascertain his or her willingness to attend at all. Occasionally I am faced with a husband (usually) or wife who really doesn't want to be here. I am then treated to a long look, up and down, with or without raised eyebrows, and a stance more akin to that of a stroppy teenager.

Of course, the other side of that coin is the humble 'thank you(s)' at the end of the treatment when they finally realise that, yes, I am fairly petite, but actually it's all in the wrist action... and my wrists are good.

Gardeners

I know the weather has changed when my clinic suddenly becomes full of 'the seasonal exerciser', who has just completed (or not) the first mow of the lawn, the clearing of the greenhouse, the dreaded weeding. *"Well, I only did an hour",* is the plaintive cry, from the usual faces. And the result is often a few trips to the osteopath. Or, in the case of one patient, who had fallen off his ladder, a fractured hip.

Kitchen Staff

On a larger scale, and not entirely irrelative to gardening injuries, a number of years ago I found myself treating about six people from the kitchen of a very famous garden in Cornwall and I began to wonder what and why. I asked if I could perhaps come in and observe them at work, with a view to suggesting appropriate adjustments within the work place. Happily, they agreed. I was somewhat alarmed at some of the practices going on there (such as the heights and levels of the equipment that staff were using and the stresses that their bodies were being put under) and made a hasty retreat home to consider how best to put forward my list of suggestions. These didn't, actually, entail a huge budget and were actually gratefully received and acted upon quickly and efficiently to the evident glee of the kitchen staff.

Tourists

During the annual Cornish holiday season, my clinic fills with injuries pertaining to packing a heavy suitcase, dragging it into the car, driving many miles to the most South Westerly point in England, dragging the suitcase out of the car into the tiny cottage or rented caravan unpacking, sleeping in an unfamiliar bed, and ambulating in a space the size of your smallest bedroom back home. Add to this the fun parks, slides, rock pools, cliff walking and the general holiday over-indulgence, and you can have the makings of a mishap or two.

Animal Lovers

Among my 'pet hates', pardon the pun, are those animal lovers who care more for their animals than they do for themselves. They typically care far more for their animals than they do for themselves, and pay little heed to my advice and education etc.

One of my patients for many years was the Head Keeper at *Newquay Zoo*. She is among the most dedicated people I know and hence her list of injuries read like every osteopath's nightmare... She would muck out, feed, shovel sand, chase and capture and then re-chase, and re-capture the animals, fight them and carry them. Commonly, she was required to rescue them from beneath buildings, down holes and under boulders, (often in the dark). She once became a surrogate mother (in her own home) to an abandoned colobus monkey, waking every couple of hours to feed it until it could go back to its cage, all the while continuing to work full-time at the zoo.

On one occasion, she strained a rib while lifting a tapir. Not many weeks later she strained it again, this time lifting a tree – yes, a tree - into the panda cage. In the very same week, on a particularly busy day, she was obliged to venture into the swan enclosure, birds being the only animals she isn't too fond of. One of the swans decided to attack her, leaving lovely shiny bruises all over her lower extremities. She had been trained to hold the swan's neck under the water to establish dominance, unfortunately with the public looking on, she was rendered helpless by the beastly bird...

Another entry simply reads: left hip pain whilst crawling under a porta-cabin looking for an escaped mongoose. The light was so poor that she only knew for sure that she had captured it when it bit her hand.... On another occasion she suffered 8,000 volts whilst climbing over the tapir enclosure fence, resulting in a blistered right leg. And then there was the crawl through the bushes to re-capture an escaped potoroo (it's a rabbit-sized marsupial).

In one particular week, which must have been a real test of endurance, she spoke of 'chasing an otter around the car park, falling over a barrier and bruising a knee' and of rescuing a lynx from a hole into which it had crawled. The lynx had to be sedated to affect its capture, rendering it unconscious temporarily, although not temporarily enough as *"his head and mine met at the same level and he began to growl.....*" Hence, the 'lift' was rather rapid, resulting in the *gleno-humeral* joint (shoulder) strain that she presented with that week.

She was once bitten on the knee by a coati, but only persuaded to go to the hospital when a colleague spotted blood leaking from her. The staff could only assume that the animal had actually eaten a chunk of her knee as they couldn't find it. The hole was so deep that it took over a month to knit together.

Her most futile, not to say embarrassing, escapade involved a seagull, which, according to a member of the public who telephoned the zoo, was 'stranded' on an island on a small lake which had recently been dredged. As a non-discriminatory animal lover, my patient duly donned a pair of waders and set off through the mud on her rescue mission. On reaching the gull she found that she had sunk so far into the mud that she couldn't move her legs and she herself became trapped in the swamp-like, twiggy mud. She had to be rescued by the fire service, an event that made the national newspapers, to her friends' and colleagues' huge amusement.

Thinking of my zoo lady will always bring a smile to my face, not because she has been responsible for some of the most bizarrely caused injuries I have treated, or because she normally has little 'welly' marks on the back of her legs, but because she is one of the most delightfully enigmatic people I have ever had the pleasure to meet.

Another patient of mine is an avid dog lover and provides a lovely home for larger canines which might otherwise have been put down. She also does the odd bit of house/animal sitting, often enduring endless nights on a strange sofa with inadequate heating and/or bedding. Her injuries are not quite as bizarre as those my zoo lady but normally result from being dragged over by some over-zealous pooch. She too is bruised from head to foot on an all too regular basis. Indeed my own dog recently managed to lasso his very thin lead around her ankle unbeknownst to her and on her command proceeded to run on ahead of her, with obvious lacerations and a sore backside resulting....

Horse riders tend to endure a greater level of abuse from their animals than most. They put up with broken ribs, being bucked, being kicked in the shins whilst grooming, have their rider 'poo pick' on a daily basis, even when eight months pregnant and suffering with *pubic symphysis dysfunction* (a very painful condition affecting the pelvis, normally during the latter months of pregnancy). And, of course, let's not forget, after getting out of bed and showering at some un-godly hour, tying back our now wet hair in a pony tail which then rests on our necks for the rest of the day (a real 'no no' for any of us hoping to avoid arthritis of the cervical spine) - all so that we can get 15 minutes in with our equine friend before heading off to work for the day.

And I cannot leave out my lovely young lady who, adamant that her pooch should get a walk, despite the ground being covered by sheets of ice and the fact that she suffers with *ankylosing spondylitis*, fell on her bum on the slippery pavement. Through the pain and agony she felt, between her fingers, something soft and squidgy...... Yup, you guessed it, the bag of dog poo that she had just extracted from the frozen grass.

I have also treated an alarming number of veterinary assistants who have to lug sedated animals, often haphazardly, across the vet's table, or worse, retrieve frozen animals awaiting collection from a very deep freezer.

Similar issues are faced by the caring professions. Lifting the elderly and dealing with special needs clients are not for the faint hearted among us. I have treated many strains and injuries pertaining to carers, nurses....even osteopaths.

Ageing and Ailments

"I can feel it in me bones" is an expression I often heard when I was a child and young adult and I used to ponder what exactly was being 'felt'. Some decades later and a few years into my career I learned exactly what 'it' was. I learned about osteo-arthritis. It affects each and every one of us differently, yet as soon as the damp air (and it's nearly always damp in Cornwall) descends upon us, my patients begin to complain.

When I set out on my voyage of physiological exploration and learning I never foresaw that I might grow to like - to cherish, even - my relationships with the older generation. During my early days, in the late '70s and '80s, we weren't encouraged to engage in conversation with older people unless we were being taught by them or being told to shut up by them. In fact, I cannot recall one conversation I had with any my grandparents. I assumed I would not find treating this particular section of the population easy, but I couldn't have been more wrong. Some of the most enigmatic and charismatic people I have met through my work have been over the age of 70, and I have been privy to many conversations that might shock even the most broadminded among you.

Many of my favourites are recorded elsewhere in the pages of this book, of course, but two stand out. One particular octogenarian told me that her small dog had attacked her new and unsuspecting postman and bitten him. Shocked and concerned for little Fred – the dog, not the postman - I asked if any further action was likely. She looked at me, with big doleful eyes, and said *"No, I just played the frail, lonely, little old lady and he immediately felt pity for me..."*

Another lady in her late 70s came for treatment on an injured shoulder. She stared at my bookcase with a puzzled expression for some time before piping up: *"why have you got so many books about whiplash on your shelves?"* I was on the point of explaining about the condition and its causes, when it dawned on me that she was under the impression that books were about bedroom behaviour rather than a spinal affliction. We dodged around this question with some fine, typical 'Englishness'.

Chapter 13:   Overloading

We are all aware of the nation's increasing obesity, among both children and adults. When faced with the evidence in clinic, I feel that it is both in the interest of the patient, as well as my responsibility in my role as a part of the care profession, to advise and educate, while also listening and acknowledging concerns, misconceptions and stigmatisation of over-weight individuals.

In many parts of the country, bariatric, or weight loss, surgery is available on the NHS, although patients are required to jump through quite a few necessary and important hoops, and undergo extensive counselling, before it can be considered, let alone carried out. This can take up to two years. There are those who believe that surgery for the overweight should not be available on the NHS, but I think that, if we discriminate against this group of patients, who is next?

Surely educating patients and regulating the often underhand food industry should be the way forward?   I once attended a lecture given by a bariatric surgeon from the West Country.   He wasn't judgemental about his patient group. He basically put obesity down to a mathematical equation, *viz,* if you eat more calories than you burn in a day, you will put on weight; all of your life. It isn't difficult really is it?

It is our duty to continuously educate overweight patients about the impact that excess weight has on the various systems of the body. Some manual therapists find it difficult to treat heavier patients, simply because they are unable physically to do so, and some decide not to at all. In my view, we should not be casting judgement on any of our patients; it is our job to help them back to health. Patients with joint problems that are likely being caused by excess weight need to be told. Yes, it's probable that they already know, but nonetheless we are duty bound to give them the facts. Patients are more likely to continue with treatment if they feel safe talking about their weight gain and diet.

Manual therapy works directly on muscles, tendons etc., accessing which requires working through layers of fat. Clearly, we all have different amounts of body fat, or *'adipose'* tissue, in which hormones are stored. These hormones carry so-called *'markers'*, which provide a range of information, from how our insulin is controlled to how we respond to attack from disease.

Our bodies react to injury and disease with inflammation. It's a signalling system to the brain to initiate a healing response. Inflammation will bring all sorts of consequences to the table in response to a cold or a cut or an infection etc. Recent evidence is beginning to suggest that each individual's weight dictates the response, regularity and numbers of these markers and, whilst this research is still relatively in its infancy, it is believed that if certain hormone markers remain regularly high as is often the case with the overweight population, it is said that they are in a chronic state of inflammation of which the implications in some could be grave indeed.

Generally, the more active we are, the easier movement and exercise becomes, promoting better circulation of all bodily fluids and, most importantly, blood flow. Blood is our lifeline; it brings with it oxygen, white blood cells to fight infection and nutrients to repair or destroy individual cell growth. As we gain more weight, we often become less active, and therefore do not burn all our daily calorific intake and potentially are risking the natural and normal influences of normal blood circulation. It follows that those people who have low markers in insulin sensitivity, anti- inflammatory and fatty acid oxidation don't do enough physical exercise and lead sedentary lifestyles. (I can feel the build up of all of the above in my bum as I write - time for a break I feel a brisk walk with the dog coming on).

Usually we have the luxury of at least half an hour with our patients, and we can talk and treat at the same time, getting to know the best hopes and worst fears, provided the patient wishes to share them with us. Every visit gives us time to encourage, explain, listen and educate and I have had some great results in boosting morale even if the 'physical' problem is slow to respond.

A walk round the block, starting a yoga class, embarking upon a fitness regime at the local leisure centre, will all make a difference. There is an excellent selection of classes on hand in my own neighbourhood, and I often make a point of going along and checking them out before recommending them. I once found myself at the local over-50s class, whose teacher is the most enthusiastic dance instructor I have encountered. Her class is very popular with gentlemen and ladies alike and she also encourages disabled clients adapting the class as necessary. I was continually glared at by the 40 or so 50 to 70-plus year–olds, as I watched from the sidelines, somewhat guiltily refraining from cavorting to the heavy beats and rhythmic pulses of Dolly Parton's *'9 to 5'*. But I did sign up for the class afterwards.

What this lady's class achieves is inspirational. It encourages an older generation to continue to enjoy exercising together and positively draws 'larger' ladies and gents into 'the circle of fitness'. She is a cut above the average and has also assisted in producing a fitness DVD for amputees. Much of her programme is focussed on seated exercise, and I have been happy to encourage my elderly and disabled patients to attend, where appropriate. It's amazing what you can do – despite age and size hindrances.

Chapter 14:   Osteopathic Jargon - Fashion and Fascia

Occasionally, osteopaths get excited. Not least when the subject turns to that of 'fascia'. They have an uncontrollable urge to talk about it endlessly and its function in the human body.   I'm no exception - one lecturer in particular seemed to come alive when delivering our fascia lectures, and it wasn't long before I saw why. It is staggering stuff.

Fascia is a connective tissue made up mostly of *collagen* which provides the body with packaging, protection, posture and passageways (*Kuchera*).   But here's an astonishing 'fascia fact':   if you removed all tissue types from a face, apart from fascia, you would still recognise whose face it was. I find this mind blowing.

Fasciae are very flexible structures, able to resist the great uni-directional tension forces that our bodies exert upon them throughout our lives. As 'body workers', we osteopaths are led to think of repetitive use in a postural sense, such us spending eight hours a day plastering or sitting at a computer, as leading to certain overloading or tensile weaknesses on particular areas of the body.

I want to use the term 'tensigrity' here, a word coined by Richard Buckminster Fuller, an American architect, in the 1960s. It derives from 'tensional integrity' and relates to the tension within any given structure, from the human body to the universe generally. It has a number of definitions, although I am concerned with only one, as found in [the Oxford English Dictionary?], viz:

[mass noun] Architecture
- the characteristic property of a stable three-dimensional structure consisting of members under tension that are contiguous and members under compression that are not:
- *[as modifier]:tensegrity construction*

When we work on 'soft tissues' we are directly affecting fascia. Why do we do this? When muscles and joints are subjected to abnormal physical load (tension) or chemical stress they have to be reinforced in some way, often by thickening, over-stretching, scarring or calcifying (slowly turning to bone); when this happens over a long period of time it can impair the function or range of the body's joints and muscles, triggering an ever-decreasing circle of compensatory patterns (i.e. another stronger part of the body takes over some of the functions). Some of these things happen as a result of ageing but some also happen because of repetitive use; the two often combine, given our modern way of life, (computers, driving, etc.)

Because we know the importance of facial membranes and the impact their pathways have on the overall tensegrity of the human form, manual therapy techniques which work directly to improve these fascial sheaths and pathways can re-align and/or strengthen 'the cracks in the surfaces', albeit sometimes temporarily, and return patients to their normal posture.

Often patients try to 'link' one pain with another. Sometimes they are right and there will be some form of link, usually due to compensatory patterns, over/under-use of another part of the body. As often as not, though, there is no logical explanation for the separate and there are no plausible or proven links. However, I have come to think of the human form rather as a balloon that is filled with water - we are, after all, 65-70% water (differing for age and mass). If you apply pressure to any part of the balloon, some of the force will be felt elsewhere in its structure. Continued pressure may lead to the effects becoming permanent and the balloon will come to rely on other areas for its ability to remain intact. Add time and ageing into the equation and you have a structure which will struggle to maintain itself. We cannot expect to defeat this natural order; however, we do aim to optimize the body's remaining 'good' functions. I am not referring to states of disease here, but physical inadequacies we all experience throughout our lives. In releasing or freeing fascia when it is placed under these excessive forces, the body's other systems, such as the circulatory and nervous systems, can function a little easier.

However, fascia doesn't like fashion. When a young lad enters your clinic with his trousers hanging around his arse your heart tends to sink. I have tried to explain that this makes them look like they are walking with a big 'jobby' in their pants, which surely cannot be good for the image, but, alas, they would prefer to remain the cool convict who, in ten years or so, will likely have a buggered lumbar spine and possibly pelvis. If it were intended we should walk like John Wayne approaching a gun duel, then indeed, we would. In fact we did, somewhere between the *hominidae* and *homo sapiens* evolutionary period (just after *bipedalism*), so perhaps this is isolated case of the devolution of a select group of trendy teenage boys and prisoners?

And as for shoes, where do I start?

There used to be a time, at least when I was training, that the biggest threat in the foot department to the lumbar spine etc. was high heels. Ooooh, nasty high heels. Evil. As it happens, I have only met one patient that struggled to get into flatter shoes having spent over 30 years in high heels.

From my clinical experience, one of the biggest threats to feet, gastrocnemius and soleus (calf) muscles, knees, hips, pelvic joints and lumbar spine, are today's fashionable flat shoes.

Let me just explain my anxiety here. When your foot strikes the floor, unless you are bare foot or wearing shoes which fit both in length and width, your brain struggles to receive vital information as to where it is 'in space'. The brain needs this feedback from the surface of the foot and its joints so that, without you even realising, it can instigate the correct sequence of events required for walking.

One of the latest 'comfy' shoe fads is a certain plastic type with lots of 'air holes' in them and a useless 'strap' at the back of the heel. They provide no stability for the foot at all, which just doesn't know if it's coming or going. Ultimately, because they are 'slip on' shoes, the toes begin to curl and claw until the tendons and bones become unable to reverse this clawing. This can mis-shape the foot by causing bunions and calluses; not good.

Another favoured type of footwear in the winter is a certain type of flat, furry boot. Whether observing patients in clinic or just watching someone walking down the street in these poorly designed boots, I can see that their feet are very often over-pronated (turned inwards). On examination of the boot, the evidence is clear - the tell-tale crease lines appearing over the width of the boot and the collapse of the heel. Because they do not fit length and width, they slip on and off as you walk in them, and they are so very flat with virtually no heel at all, you have no choice but to walk flat footed, scuffing your heel on the floor, and dragging your leg behind you. This means your calf muscles endure too much load in the walking process, in time often resulting in enlarged calf muscles and making it quite difficult and painful sometimes to point your toes.

If this all sounds a bit serious, it's because it is. Those of you who like this type of flat, ill-fitting shoe tend to wear them all the time and your body is struggling to adapt to them.

The latest trend among the younger female population, which I fear the 'wag' celebrity genre of women may be responsible for, requires the fashion follower to purchase an over-priced, over-sized and over-filled carpet-bag, which is then draped modishly over the arm (at the elbow joint) in the 'sling' position – at least while on public view.... .

I must be very old, you're thinking? Well, at forty-four, I like to think not. I like some clothing fashions, too - occasionally. But it never ceases to dumbfound me that the one change people find themselves unable to commit to in lifestyle adaptation relates to what they are wearing. Please, please, ensure your loved ones' shoes fit them correctly, in both length *and width*. It may save you a visit to a manual therapist/podiatrist in years to come.....

Chapter 15:   Placebo and Manual Therapy

So, I'll probably rant a little here, but this subject is very important to me. The placebo, a subject of much debate and research, is a decisive 'utensil' in my first aid kit.

Astonishingly, it continues to be spoken of in cautionary terms by some of our medical colleagues, who may still see it in the same context as the 'quackery' that was prevalent a hundred years and more ago. Patrick Wall cites its first use back in 1340, and its association with the term *'hocus pocus'*. He says: "It is often associated with 'doing nothing' and it has been suggested to be nothing more than Pavlovian conditioning."*

He continues: "Placebo is not a stimulus but an appropriate action. As such, the placebo terminates and cancels the sense expressed in terms of possible action. Pain is then best seen as a need state, like hunger and thirst which can be terminated".

*The Pavlovian Dog experiments, conducted by Ivan Pavlov, introduced bell-ringing at feeding time for dogs, when they would naturally salivate (this is part of the para-sympathetic nervous system – meaning it works without your conscious thought). He discovered that bell ringing outside of feed times would then also lead to salivation, suggesting that salivation had become a conditioned response or reflex to the bell-ringing. Some equate the placebo response to this unconscious reaction.

Yet, even medicine and medical research have placebo in their armoury. 'Big- pharma' as it is often abbreviated (large pharmaceutical corporations) devise shrewd ways to make some drugs look more powerful than others, such as introducing the psychology of colour to the pills. The more colour, the more placebo being conjured.

However, placebo continues to baffle its critics. In medical terms, there is no general consensus of its capabilities, its limits and its effect on us as individuals. Nor are there precise guidelines on its use in a 'treatment' sense. But, whilst the matter remains in professional and ethical limbo, we have used and do use placebo in trials for new drugs, dental, surgical procedures and manual therapy techniques.

Some of my patients are suffering undulating fits of agony when they make an appointment. (By the way, I rarely see them on the same day, because it's generally difficult to make sense of their complaint, due to their loss of lucidity). After ensuring they aren't a case for A&E, plying them with advice and agreeing to see them within the next 24-48 hours, I can find that, when they arrive for the appointment, their pain has all but disappeared and they are calm and logical, panic over.   For many, this could have happened as a natural response to taking some form of analgesia or anti-inflammatory, and following a few other simple instructions. For some, though, it is that their natural learned response to pain has always been to 'panic' (mostly unnecessarily).   Their recovery will have been the result of having some structure to focus on and someone to share their pain and fear with. And there are some who would call this the placebo response.

I once accompanied a very dear friend of mine who suffers with multiple sclerosis to a hospital appointment, not as her osteopath but as her friend (and, often, indeed, her memory). My friend introduced me to the nurse as an osteopath, rather than as a friend, unaware, as was I, of any stigma that might be attached to the treatment choices MS patients make. How naive we were. The nurse evidently felt threatened enough to dismiss my knowledge and expertise – "well, that's only placebo."

I did not take the bait. We were not there to discuss the power of placebo but to review my friend's *gabapentin* levels, her fatigue and the number of UTIs (urinary tract infections) she was experiencing. In truth, there was nothing that this nurse knew about MS that I did not. Through her own inexperience, and possibly fear, she resorted to insult.

I feel reasonably up-to-date with medical advances for MS sufferers. Having volunteered for some time at the Cornish 'Merlin Project', specifically built to provide care, treatment and support for MS sufferers, I am aware that various types of medicine keep MS patients out of much of the pain that they may otherwise suffer, and that botox is now having a positive effect in lowering incontinence incidence. Herein lies the difference between the nurse and the osteopath. I am informed as to both the orthodox and 'unorthodox' approach to MS treatment. She only seemed to be aware of the former. Nurses need to be kept 'in the know'. There is no room for egos in caring for patients. We don't yet fully understand the aetiology of multiple sclerosis, it is still being posited and theorised. Should we not be working together?

Yes, I do treat patients with MS and, no, some of them are not going to get better in the long term, but talking to them in a positive way, treating their often contracted and contorted muscles and being supportive can do much for morale as opposed to being told "there is no more to be done" or "there are no more drugs". This is why there is such a plethora of 'alternatives'. They may be un-trialled and unproven in the world of medicine, but 'alternatives' often offer more 'care', more understanding and have more time. "There's nothing more to be done" or "let's see if we can make your body and mind work as optimally as possible" - I know what I would want to hear.

What we have to remember is that we don't always credit placebo where we should. Sometimes, a sympathetic ear, or perhaps a shoulder to cry on, is no more than a patient needs to be 'cured' – but it's hardly something that you can trumpet!

One example of placebo which springs to mind is the case of a lady who presented to my clinic with mid-thoracic spine (mid-back) pain. She was finding it difficult to move her upper body and deep inspiration (breathing in) was causing this part of her spine to 'pinch'. She arrived with a case worker, not because she had been in trouble but because, over the previous five years, she had been regularly beaten by her husband, and she was now living in a women's refuge. She found it difficult to talk and she was incredibly frail, leaving me to wonder "how on earth am I going to be able to put my hands on her?"

Ninety per cent of our treatment time was spent talking and explaining what I do and why, and the rest getting her to breathe in and out properly. When she got up her pain had gone and she was moving normally. It was the only visit she needed.

Obviously, this does not happen very often. I am not a miracle worker I didn't wave a magic wand or lay 'healing hands' on her. That appointment could have gone any way, very badly or no outcome at all. I believe much of her anxiety and reaction to the physical abuse had been bound up in her muscles for a number of years (the over-facilitation that I referred to earlier in this book), and she was on the verge of hyper-ventilating due to her anxiety levels. The breathing exercises would have helped, but I knew I needed to get her to trust me before I even went near her, and it was probably much more about what I said (or didn't say) than what I did.

This is placebo and how to exploit it. Although, of course, I did have clinical knowledge to back up what came out of my mouth and to apply the techniques.

Every day in clinic, I witness patients with umpteen negative experiences and a variety of attitudes to pain. After all, who wants to be in pain? 'It prevents me from earning a living'; 'it makes me hurt'; 'it makes me miserable'. We all know about pain. Most pain that I see in my practice is mend-able, do-able, manageable, not end of the world-able. With some investment from the patient and a treatment or two, most pain will go away. Yes, occasionally I request the GP to prescribe this or that drug to speed things up, but mostly it will go away, and once patients realise this they calm down, their soft tissues relax and life gets a whole lot easier. I accept that this is not always the case, but an awful lot of the time it is, and we are trained well enough to recognise and filter those that don't fit this pattern. Attitude plays a big part in a patient's recovery. The real, physical work that manual therapists do reduces the mess left behind after a lateral collateral ligament knee strain, or the gluteal muscle tension caused as an elderly patient struggles to avoid an incontinence accident by squeezing his or her buttocks all day, or improves the *proprioception* (disorientation) caused by a torn ankle ligament.

It has been claimed that placebo response will reduce on repetition. A fearful patient arrives, anxious and nervous; you go through your protocol and reassure, etc., and manage the fear for many months, or even years. And then the patient loses faith and hope, and the fear and anxiety surface again. This may well happen in response to life-changing events (birth or death of loved ones, divorce etc.), which can be enough to tip the balance, and often the cycle will begin again. But does it invalidate the original exercise? I don't think so.

Pain and fear need to be explained, challenged and managed throughout our lives. We should be encouraged to rationalise them and adapt our learned responses to them, even if they include the use of placebo, for we will dip in and out of pain and fear all our lives.

Our bodies produce various 'stimuli' in the nervous system in order to provoke an awaited response; this could be phrased as a cause and effect, or, action, reaction. Often these responses are termed 'learned responses'. Our bodies and minds learn how to respond to a stimulus and this response is then stored away for the next occasion it is needed. If that response is placebo and it is understood by our bodies to work and rid us of the pain why would we ignore or even abuse it?

However you measure placebo, don't underestimate it or write it off as some alternative, healing hands or spiritualism 'bullshit'. It's real, it exists and people like that nurse should maybe take a look in their 'first aid kit' occasionally to see what's lacking, because it's free and has a function.

Chapter 16:   The Pain Game

Pain presents in many forms. This chapter refers to pain types as seen in a 'typical' manual therapy clinic, not those experienced through life-threatening, oncologic (cancer) or advanced neurological conditions, such as motor neurone disease. However, all manual therapists treat patients with terminal conditions, whether while undergoing cancer treatment or with life-long and progressive painful conditions such as rheumatoid arthritis (RA) and *ankylosying spondylitis* (AS).

Humble manual therapists and neurophysiologists would all agree on one thing, I'm sure (hooray) - that pain is subjective. It means different things to different people. Besides tissue trauma, it can, for example, indicate a surge of emotion or simply hunger. Who hasn't felt a physical twinge on hearing bad news, or suffered severe discomfort from an empty stomach. There are hundreds of words and inferences used to describe it, because everyone's experience of it is slightly different.

Phrases such as "no pain, no gain" and "what doesn't kill me, makes me stronger" have deeper implications than you might imagine – it is pain that has helped us develop our capacity for compassion and care.

We now live in an electronic world where, not only do we demand, and expect, immediate answers but where experiences can be easily compared and extremes identified. This can lead to misinformation, misdiagnosis and, as often as not, leaves the public confused. Of course, advertising and the media play a part in this, taking a small piece of research (often in its early stages – a time when it will generate more misleading results) and distorting its original meaning. But when it comes to the matter of pain, we really want that quick fix promised by the powerful world of media.

We don't listen to, or are as reassured by, the doctor as was the case with our parents. We question them, we question our respect for them; the relationship between us has altered. 'White coat syndrome' has all but disappeared in the 21st century. Health resources are becoming exhausted, as the population in the UK ages rapidly and therefore makes increasing demands on them.

Patients are often left searching for answers to what, in a bio-mechanical sense, are not difficult questions, but which are posed in the wrong places. Frequently, post-surgical patients will present to me unsure of how to manage their recovery, i.e. how or when to begin using a repaired limb or joint, because the health system does not have the resources to deal with these post operative questions. Therapies are popping up here, there and everywhere, becoming more and more obscure, and we're all left struggling to maintain what is real therapy and what is not. Searching for the 'cure' has reached epidemic proportions and, as we have seen, almost anything goes, fads coming and going almost monthly. People's rationality all but disappears in their desperate search for a solution to their pain/condition.

I have had patients who have demanded that I treat them with a particular technique or other, or who are so desperate in their search for answers that they insist on coming in two or three times a week, and for months on end. These are difficult situations to manage but managed they must be. Leading someone gently to the conclusion that they are not going to find an answer is a delicate matter. Helping them understand that they must learn to manage their pain takes not only time, but also a practitioner who has featured at least somewhere in his or her pain journey. It's not easy to be told by a complete stranger, no matter how qualified, that 'you need to learn to live with it'.

Unless managed in its entirety, pain can impact on your life in many different ways.

1)	Alienation: initially, everyone is on your side, you invoke sympathy and compassion from fellow sufferers, family and friends. When it's prolonged over years, however, you begin to exhaust the patience of those loved ones and often this can lead to resentment by those involved..

Friends and family eventually run out of steam, become less supportive and may even ostracize you. They leave you out of the loop, because they've run out of things to say about your pain, and the subject is best avoided.

Probably, one of the unkindest insults a chronic pain sufferer has to endure is 'labelling'. In today's society, there is stigma attached to being unable to live normally and hold down an occupation due to pain, with little being done to encourage the willing disabled worker.

2)	Depression: one of the worst cases of chronic, unmanaged pain I have witnessed involved a very young man who, six years previously, had been horrifically kicked near to death in an unprovoked attack in broad daylight. He returned to his very manual occupation a few months after the incident, but became less and less able to carry out his work, due to lower lumbar pain. However, an MRI failed to identify a problem. He was eventually signed off work indefinitely by his GP and his back pain continued to worsen until he was able to walk no more than about 20 yards before he was forced to sit down. My point is that, aside from his lumbar spine diagnosis, which was never confirmed, no-one gave any thought to his mental health and when he presented to me he was clearly a very anxious and fearful young man. No, he didn't want to go back to work, but then he didn't really want to go out at all. His experience of pain and fear had not been addressed and he was a quivering mess with a bad back. People (including his GP surgery) had already judged him. In their eyes, he was possibly a malingerer – and this in turn exacerbated his desperate state.

3)   Anger: - this can be exhausting for a patient in continuous pain, using up precious energy that would be better fed into management of the pain. I've seen some

desperately angry patients, wailing *'Why me?'*, when they might be better served working on how to manage the situation.

In his book, *'The Culture of Pain 1993'*, David Morris explores the tragedy of pain in today's world. He writes: "The reason why doctors and writers and all of us should think about tragic pain is because as a culture, we are rapidly losing an understanding of tragedy". "As a culture", he says, "we do not take kindly to the tragic vision. We tacitly reject it." He goes on to point out that tragedy and suffering are all around us, everyday.

Modern day communication systems ensure we are kept aware of it every single day. However, we can be emotionally moved by fictitious tragedy or 'real life' gratuitous television than by the suffering on our own doorsteps.

As I see it, we could all do with reviewing our attitude to pain. It is a tool to learn from, learn not only about the world's attitude to and treatment of pain, but also about ourselves. If we continue to rely on a one-dimensional approach to treating pain (the pill), we are disempowering ourselves and fooling ourselves into thinking we have 'dealt' with it. We leave the painful episode none the wiser – and are unprepared for the next onset.

Our pain is as unique to us as our DNA, conditioned by pre-pain experience, childhood pain, death of a loved one, attitude, and expectation. We can explain it away anatomically and physiologically, by researching the primary sensory cortex, the *spinothalamic tract*, the *prostaglandins* and neuro-transmitters and so on, but pain will always be unique to the individual. Torn meniscus discs will have a similar physiological effect on each and every one of us, but the impact and implications of that pain will be unique. To one person, it may mean being unable to walk with a group of like minded friends once a week (perhaps their only pleasure), while to another it will be the inability to bring in a wage for a young family. But, as far as the patient's case history notes are concerned, it will present simply as a 'meniscus tear'.

David Morris argues that chronic physical pain and emotion should be treated together, as there is strong evidence to suggest that emotions and trauma can either suppress or elevate pain levels. I have witnessed this in clinic and in my own personal life.

One patient of mine developed lower leg pain particularly in the second year of his degree in podiatry. He described anxiety in general and the pain worsened when driving a car. After some time, and having been thoroughly checked for all obvious causes as an outpatient, it transpired that, when travelling with his grandmother in the back seat of a car as a child, she would squeeze his legs so hard - because she was frightened of travelling – that they would bruise. Seemingly, with no 'medical' answers, his pain was likely caused by stress and was probably symbolic.

After all, we all accept that phantom pregnancy exists, that strong emotional yearning for a child produces actual physical symptoms of pregnancy.

However, we are still not thinking, accepting, researching or treating patients accordingly. 'Holistic' is a bit of a dirty word in the medical world. GPs treating the body rarely treat the mind, while doctors of the mind rarely treat the body. There are obviously exceptions here, time and resources are as always the forefront of our limitations.

I believe pain scales, which purport to measure degrees of pain, are, at best, only the roughest of guides and, at worst, a waste of money.   Mood, stress and financial commitments, for example, can skew the intended results dramatically, as can the fact that pain is often episodic, and related to 'doing too much' in the garden or having an exceptionally 'heavy' day at work. They do not always require medical intervention. The body is asked to do the odd thing 'differently' and for longer periods than normal at times and these can result in the "same old problem" So pain scales here become a little 'learned' .

They could be regarded as mildly useful in confirming a patient's progressing recovery (but nothing patients cannot tell you for themselves), or provide a vague 'score' when analysing trial data, but, in my view, are not conclusive when the condition is worsening or not improving. They do, however, make sense when communicating with children, or non-English speaking patients and *somewhere* there is logic that practitioners should be using the same terminology to describe pain. But pain evaluation is much more than just determining pain and disability highs and lows. It's also about knowing a little of patient expectation levels, anxiousness, is there someone at home for them? Things you cannot interpret in a self-assessment questionnaire.

Pain scales have evolved over time and come in many forms. One of the first was the *Dolorimeter*, first used around 1940. This was a questionnaire, which took its name from *'dolor'*, an old English word for pain. Currently in the UK, most people dealing with patients in pain are required to participate in the VAS (visual analogue scale), which rates pain out of 10. It is succinct in its delivery of self-assessment, but rather meaningless when assessing how a patient should be treated for their pain – mostly because pain alters daily and weekly for many sufferers.

The National Institute for Clinical Excellence used the *Roland Morris Disability* questionnaire when 'measuring' for lower lumbar pain. It asks specific questions of the patient, but only records how they feel on the day of the questionnaire completion, which is beyond my rationale completely. The 24 questions focus around statements that patients tick if relevant to how they feel that day. "As you read the list, think of yourself *today*. When you read a sentence that describes you today, put a tick against it. If the sentence does not describe you, then leave the space blank and go on to the next one. Remember, only tick the sentence if you are sure it describes you today".

I'm unsure how this information is useful or valid as we all know pain does not always present the same every day. Is this as far as we have come in the 21st century in pain assessment?

Although no longer used, the *McGill-Melzack Pain Questionnaire* blinded patients with a homogenous mass of about 80 negative words (gnawing, cruel, killing) asking them to chose up to seven of them which described their own experience of their pain. Conclusions were then drawn from the answers Obviously the words were chosen in an attempt to identify pain 'types' such as neurogenic etc., but the analysis of this information is entirely subjective – an interpretation of pain is not an exact science. They all seem to fail in acknowledging the individual's experience of their pain.

Most of us know of someone who likes to talk about pain, most of us want to share our experiences of it, most of us want to know about it, the 'edgy stuff', the trauma of it, things you perhaps haven't experienced yourself. We like to compare. When patients visit me in pain they *want* to talk about it, they've exhausted their family who are sick to the hind teeth of hearing about it. They want to explore the *'how'*s, the *'why'*s and the *'what'*s, to tell me they are suffering; they don't like being interrupted until they have explained in minuscule detail how much it bloody hurts! We absolutely deny patients this part of the pain experience by popping them in the waiting room with a form to fill out.

Chapter 17:   The Flying Osteopath

I wanted to leave this chapter to the end, even though it is chronologically out of place, because it evokes so many very happy memories. I believe I was at my most resourceful when I was living in our isolated home in Spain, and it gave me inspiration for the following years in more ways than one. In particular, I began to write again (I had long stopped keeping any sort of journal), recording our experience of living in the mainly non-English-speaking, extremely rural hamlet of Arroyo de Priego, near Iznajar, Cordoba in the hills of southern Spain.

However, the heartfelt desire to stay in Spain finally gave in to the cold logistical and economic reasons for leaving towards the end of my fourth year summer term and a looming fifth year of virtual full-time existence in London. As far as the family unit was concerned, the adults were up to their necks in financial and logistical problems - and the children's verve had begun to wane after a two week trip to England and more importantly Cornwall. A few hours over the Tamar Bridge and we all felt the tug of the West Country once more.

During my fourth year of training and while still in Spain I worked as a 'physical therapist' (a now 'protected' title in the UK – protected by physiotherapists). As I have said, I had gained a massage qualification in my first year, which enabled me to obtain sufficient insurance cover to get my hands on patients, even though most of my local patients knew me as an osteopath. This did not worry me too much as, at the time, it was not necessary to have authorisation to use the title in Spain - and I was not performing any 'dodgy HVLA/HVTs'...

I often found myself bartering a treatment for a lesson in Spanish anatomy, learning catch phrases like *'boca arriba'* (face up) which helped the treatment sessions along no end. I found work two hours away in *Estepona*, at a five star hotel with a 'health centre' attached. I endured the drive once a week, and also found myself motoring back and forth within a 40 mile radius of our village to bring in what money I could to fund the seemingly endless cost of my education.

This brought with it the obvious (and some not so obvious) pitfalls of treating ex-pats who had fled England for the sun, sea and sangria, and I would often find myself, in the middle of the day, trying to wedge my treatment couch into a tiny space within the mobile or static home of some inebriated early starter. Suddenly all of my hepatic and respiratory learning would take on a 3D vantage point as I would try and conduct a case history whilst my patient and his family would sit in the said confined space and smoke their way through a packet of Bensons. Commencement of the sweaty process of treating these patients would trigger the emergence of a thick emulsifying odour of stale whiskey, as they perspired profusely. Yum. I wasn't at all deluded into thinking that I had any chance of changing this lifestyle 'improvement' I might add. I was just checking - and hoping for their sake that the pain in the shoulder was not emanating from a screaming liver.

One gent, I remember, was living in a mobile home whilst his house was being built and I treated him fairly regularly for various musculoskeletal presentations. He had fled Ireland having divorced his long term wife, who, seemingly, had succeeded in relieving him of a handsome sum of money. He was fairly set on seeing his days out in a state of highs and lows brought on by cannabis and alcohol. He did have the capacity to be able to smile and joke at his own misfortune and this tended to make things a tad easier each visit. Given the lack of space available in his mobile home, treatment often commenced outside in the car park, much to the amusement of his fellow campers. His avid consumption of alcohol often resulted in him falling off the couch, and frequently being stung by the ever-present wasps. Each visit would conclude with my remonstrations about his drinking, cannabis use and a blood pressure reading – a combination that really ought to have confirmed him as dead.

Eventually, after constant persuasion, he reluctantly visited his doctor, if only to have his blood pressure read and treated. On my way back from Estepona one evening through Marbella's endless stream of traffic, I pulled off the road for a coffee I received a phone call from his doctor. It transpired that he was very concerned because his patient had just confessed to him, in very poor Spanish, that he had killed his wife.... I was able to enlighten the doctor, to the effect that, actually, his patient was going through a traumatic divorce, was drinking too much, that I feared his blood pressure was about to catapult out of control …

and that his wife, as far as I knew, was very much with the living (and now, dare I say the sane).

Word quickly spread through our tiny village (mainly through my wonderful neighbour Dolores avid trips up to our house) and I was soon treating many of the olive farming community, as well as ex-pats.

Dolores was a small, elderly but very vociferous farmer's wife with many grown up children, and with no English at all. *Doler* means 'to hurt' in Spanish, and she certainly lived up to her name. She would come staggering up our hill holding her back and exclaiming her customary "*mi duele*" (my pain), and I would usually treat her with some soft tissue work. In return she would, either look after my daughter whilst I was in London studying, provide us with a freshly killed turkey at Christmas or allow us to wander over her land looking for '*lena*' (firewood).

A few months after my arrival in Spain, before I had carved an osteopathic niche in these Andalucían hills, I had to attend an interview some 90 kilometres away in Fuengirola. Dolores, who rarely left the village but who had family in Fuengirola, offered to accompany me, so long as she could stop off to see her sister in Los Boliches. I agreed, although my Spanish was still a work-in-progress at this juncture. It was the first time I had seen Dolores out of her trade mark farmer's wife pinafore - she looked surprisingly current. On reaching Fuengirola, we spent an hour and a half trying to find the interview address. When we finally arrived, I didn't like the look of the place and suggested that we go straight to her sister's house. Another hour and we arrived in Los Boliches, to rapturous applause from what must have been her entire family. There were hordes of them....

Dolores introduced me to each and every one of them. They were fanatically welcoming (as anyone who knows Spain can attest), but they chattered at speeds I thought were only attainable by light itself and there was no way I was able to keep up. I smiled empathically in what I thought were the right places; phrases where *"Amanda"* was used, for example and I repeated the little Spanish I knew over and over...

We were to be fed - an integral part of Spanish culture, I had already learned. So, little old vegetarian me (which they all thought ludicrous) munched her way through copious amounts of manchego cheese, bread and olives, etc. Plate after plate of food kept arriving and I was encouraged to eat, eat, eat! When passed a huge plate of whitebait in batter (my worst living nightmare!) I was told to *"tome lo"*, (take it!"). Fish I can do, on occasion, but fish bone, eyes, guts and fin I cannot; so *'la Ingles'* was left trying to nibble the flesh from the whitebait (have you tried it?) and feign appreciation - to the astonishment and utter delight of my Spanish *compadres.*

Finally, just when I thought my ordeal was over, we were all called to the kitchen. For dinner....!! Awaiting me was the most gargantuan portion of egg and chips. *Mr Creosote* from *Monty Python* had not a patch on what I was about to endure. I ate myself into such a stupor through not wanting to seem ungrateful or insult the cook that my stomach was inches from eruption. I did have the good sense not to 'take' from the ritualistic bread passing phase and politely declined the desserts that followed. It was an endless feasting.

When, at last, I was sure the feeding was over and we were all sat back in the lounge of the tiny flat, the conversation turned, I think, to me. Dolores was explaining that I had treated her with what she termed *'masaje'* (massage). I assumed she was saying this because she was emulating the movements on her own body. The only parts of my body that were capable of moving comfortably were my eyes, which were betraying my confusion, and my lips which were smiling wearily.

Dolores suddenly leapt up from the couch, grabbed my hand and led me into one of the very small dark bedrooms off the main lounge. She bounced across the tiny bed and, lying down and patting the bed beside her, looked at me with a big grin on her face. I assumed that having just spoken about *'masaje'*, she now required one and I sat on the side of the bed, forlorn at the prospect of moving my tummy around. She sensed my desolation, however, and laughed out loud (she knew my stomach was fit to burst) and said *"No, es siesta Amanda!"*

And so the afternoon was played out, rather surreally, with me lying on a bed with an elderly Spanish lady in the dark, looking up at the ceiling, unable to sleep, perplexed and contemplating the day, and my life in Spain.

Appendix:

The Cochrane Library is considered to be one of the most advanced and complete medical databases available today. It is not necessary to work in the medical world to use it - It's available to everyone. It is extremely informative and I recommend that you to take a look before deciding whether to take your fish oil supplements, undergo the latest eye surgery or even commit to cosmetic procedures. It comprises six individual databases which between them provide "the most up-to-date, independent, high quality evidence to inform health care decision making". One of these databases, *The NHS Economic Evaluation Database,* provides the medical world with reviews of both the effectiveness and value for money of available treatments, interventions and medicines - and is therefore one of the tools used by the NHS when considering what to 'buy' or 'back'.

The database that is perhaps of more interest to readers here is the one known as Systematic Reviews, which contains a collection of trials with the same similar treatment types, surgical procedures and medicine research papers from other databases such as PubMed/Medline or EMBASE, which have slightly different remits. Singularly, research papers are often based on only a small group of patients due, amongst other things, to funding or time restraints. The systematic review effectively gathers them all and analyses them as if they were one entire review. Occasionally, you may even come across a systematic review of systematic reviews due to the sheer number of research papers accumulated over the years (these are termed meta-analyses). Systematic reviews date back only as far as 2005 so all are therefore considered current.

I have collated all the available (at the time of writing) systematic reviews covering manual therapy techniques, from the Cochrane systematic review database and provided the reader with the author's conclusion at the foot of each listing. I have been unable to substantiate randomisation, bias, inclusion criteria etc as there are so many papers and reviews listed, but I do urge the reader to look more closely at the evidence provided by these reviews.

As I mentioned, many manual therapy trials involve more than one technique; for example, each 'thrusting technique and exercise' has been collated with papers that are simply 'thrusting'. In my view, this is not a like-for- like comparison, nor does it achieve similarity to how a patient in real life would receive treatment in a manual therapy clinical setting. I therefore think this is a serious flaw in determining outcomes for these types of systematic reviews. Manual therapy is not medicine. Moreover, as highlighted earlier, the reviews are comparing patients that have "low back pain" with those that have "pelvic pain", none of which have an identifiable diagnosis. One person's low back pain may be caused by an annular tear (rip in the wall of the disc), while another's - in the same trial - may be no more than 'tight' lower back muscles or age-related degeneration. The same treatment would not be appropriate for both. Until these reviews reduce the potential for these flaws of this type, results will continue to be skewed. As you will deduce, some of the author's conclusions say 'yes the outcomes are encouraging', some say 'maybe' and some say there is no evidence that they work at all. This is not exactly helpful in determining the efficacy of manual therapy.

Of course, in all realms of science each research paper can be rapidly superseded by the next. Trial after trial stacks up over the years until, sometimes many decades later, a general consensus among the profession or drug on trial will be deemed – it is an evolving process. All trials are supposed not to contain bias, (or influence of any party involved), although they often do, and 'randomisation' - the selection process of patients - is meant to be just that: random. Again, this is not unfortunately always the case.

A recent systematic review of systematic reviews (Posadski, June 2012), entitled "Is Spinal Manipulation Effective for Pain? An Overview", identified 22 systematic reviews and concluded that it (spinal manipulation) "fails to demonstrate that it is an effective intervention for pain management". Note: spinal manipulation, not manual therapy. The review of the reviews goes on: "the limitation of this review was that publication bias may have been inherited". And so a very important, and not to say expensive, review of reviews may have been potentially distorted.

In contrast two years earlier, a conglomeration of UK and US evidence in a study entitled *"Effectiveness of Manual Therapies: The UK Evidence Report", (Bronfort G., et al. Feb 2010)*, reviewed 49 systematic reviews (among others) which included techniques such as spinal manipulation (HVT) and soft tissue mobilisations; it concluded "manual therapy is effective in adults for some specific conditions such as low back pain, migraine, cervicogenic dizziness". It begs the question "what has changed in two years"?

In other words, just how helpful is such a large compendium of non-heterogeneous experiences?

Furthermore, and just to put the proverbial cat among the pigeons, a review of the use of *transcutaneous electrical nerve stimulation* (TENS) by D.M. Walsh et al. 2009, looking at 1,775 papers, of which only twelve, totalling 919 participants, met the inclusion criteria, concluded: "there is insufficient evidence to draw any conclusions about the effectiveness of TENS as an isolated treatment of acute pain in adults". Yet this is a treatment backed and funded by our health system. Once again, this focussed exclusively on the use of the TENS machine. (I do know that some patients have great results using the TENS machine, some in isolation and some as part of an integrated package of pain care.)

All systematic reviews on The Cochrane Library website were considered at length in the categories of Complementary Therapy, Orthopaedics and Neurology; specific search words were not necessary as **every** entry was checked and included if it was within the remit of manual therapy techniques. (Although, if readers can identify others please do let me know). Papers involving children under the age of 12 were not used.

1. Non-invasive physical treatments for chronic/recurrent headache (aged 12-78). Bronfort et al. 2009

   Authors' Conclusions: May be effective, further scientific rigorous methods required.

2. Spinal Manipulation for dysmenorrhoea. Proctor et al. 2010

Authors' Conclusions: No evidence for efficacy.

3. Manipulative therapy (osteopathic, chiropractic, respiratory therapists and physiotherapists) for asthma. Hondras et al. 2009
   Authors' Conclusions: Insufficient evidence – more adequately sized random controlled trials required. Insufficient evidence to support or refute use.

4. Massage and touch for dementia. Hansen et al. 2008
   Authors' Conclusions: May serve as alternative for complementary to other therapies for the management of behavioural, emotional and perhaps other conditions associated with dementia. More research required.

5. Combined chiropractic interventions for low back pain. Walker et al. 2010
   Authors' Conclusions: Slightly improved pain and disability in short term and pain the medium term for acute and sub-

acute; no evidence to support or refute that those interventions provide clinically meaningful difference when compared to other interventions.

6. Interventions for preventing and treating pelvic and back pain in pregnancy. Examining the effects of pregnancy specific exercises, physiotherapy, acupuncture and pillows. Pennick et al 2008

   Authors' Conclusions: Some bias potential, however adding pregnancy specific exercises, physiotherapy or acupuncture to usual prenatal care appears to relieve back or pelvic pain although effects are small.

7. Massage for low back pain. Furlan et al. 2010

   Authors' Conclusions: Might be beneficial for patients with sub-acute and chronic, non-specific lower back pain, especially when combined with exercises and education. More studies required.

*Main results were interesting; they showed massage to be superior to joint mobilisation, relaxation therapy, physical therapy, acupuncture and self-care education. Reflexology of no benefit on pain reduction and function.

8. Spinal manipulative therapy for chrolower back pain. Rubinstein et al. 2011.

Authors' Conclusions: High quality evidence suggests that there is no clinically relevant difference between spinal manipulative therapy and other interventions for reducing pain and improving function in patients with chronic lower back pain. Determining cost-effectiveness of care has high priority. Further research is required.

*Main results. No serious complications observed. No data on recovery, return-to-work, quality of life and cost of care. Results demonstrate spinal manipulative therapy is as effective as other common therapies prescribed for chronic lower back pain such as exercise therapy, standard medical care and physiotherapy. Approx 2/3 of studies were at risk of bias.

Draw your own conclusions here. How useful is this review?

9. Spinal manipulation therapy for low back pain. Assendelft et al. 2008

   Authors' Conclusions: No evidence to suggest that spinal manipulative therapy is superior to other standard treatments for patients with acute or chronic lower back pain.

Does this read the same as the one above, three years later?

10. Interventions for treating chronic ankle instability. Vries et al. 2011

   Authors' Conclusions: Neuromuscular training alone appears to be effective in the short term but whether this advantage would persist on longer term follow up is no known.

11. Deep transverse friction massage, (DTFM) for treating tendonitis. Brosseau et al. 2009

   States it's used by physiotherapists, whereas most manual therapists use it!

   Authors' Conclusions: DTFM combined with other physiotherapy modalities (ultrasound, rest, stretching, cryotherapy) compared to the other modalities alone did not show consistent benefit over pain, improvement of grip strength and functional status. Further trials, larger sample sizes required.

   Osteopaths, chiropractors and physiotherapists all use the combined modalities and probably wouldn't just use friction massage as a stand-alone treatment.

12. Therapeutic ultrasound for treating patellofemoral pain syndrome. Brosseau et al. 2009

Compares ultrasound against placebo or another intervention in patients with patellofemoral pain syndrome.

Authors' Conclusions: Not shown to have clinically important effect on pain for patients with patellofemoral pain syndrome. Conclusions limited by poor reporting of therapeutic application of ultrasound and low methodological quality. More well designed studies required.

13. Exercise therapy for chronic fatigue syndrome. Edmonds et al. 2010

    Authors' Conclusions: There is encouraging evidence that some patients may benefit from exercise therapy and no evidence that exercise therapy may worsen outcomes.

14. Exercise therapy for multiple sclerosis 260 patients. Rietberg et al. 2009

    Authors' Conclusions: The results of the present review suggest that exercise therapy can be beneficial for patients not experiencing an exacerbation. Further studies should include control for 'dose', type of ms, outcome measures and include sufficient contrast between experimental and control groups.

15. Physical therapy for [Bell's P:alsy (idiopathic facial paralysis). Tiexera et al. 2011

Involving any physical therapy, any age. Outcome measures: incomplete recovery at six months, motor synkinesis, crocodile tears or facial spasm 6 months after onset, incomplete recovery after 1 year and adverse effects attributable to the intervention.

Manual therapy interventions included: facial exercises and physical therapy with acupuncture.

Authors' Conclusions: No high quality evidence to support benefit or harm from any physical therapy. Low quality evidence that tailored facial exercises can help to improve facial function for those with moderate paralysis.

16. Non-surgical treatment (other than steroid) for carpal tunnel syndrome. O'Connor et al. 2009

Treatments studied were: a hand brace, ultrasound, oral medications, vitamin B6, yoga and carpal bone mobilisation.

Authors' Conclusions: Current evidence shows significant short-term benefits from oral steroids, splinting, ultrasound and carpal bone mobilisation. More trials needed to compare treatments and ascertain the duration of benefit.

17. Conservative treatments for whiplash. Verhayen et al. 2010

Authors' Conclusions: The trials for this review were poorly available and no pooling was achievable. These approaches remain unsupported/inconclusive.

18. Exercises for mechanical neck disorders. Kay et al. 2009

Authors' Conclusions: There is a role for exercises in the treatment of acute and chronic mechanical neck disorder and headache. Exercises for neck disorders with radicular findings are not assessed. More research in identifying the most effective treatment characteristics and dosages needed.

19. Manipulation or mobilisation for neck pain. Gross et al. 2010

    Authors' Conclusions: cervical spine mobilisation and manipulation produced similar changes. Either may provide immediate or short term change, no long term data are available. Thoracic spine manipulation may improve pain and function. Optimal techniques and dosage are unresolved.

20. Massage for mechanical neck disorders. Haraldsson et al. 2008

    12 of 19 studies were assessed as low quality.

Authors' Conclusions: No recommendations for practice can be made at this time because of the effectiveness of massage for neck pain remain uncertain.

21. Mechanical traction for cervical spine pain with or without radiculopathy. Graham et al. 2010

    Authors' Conclusions: Does not support or refute the efficacy or effectiveness of continuous or intermittent traction for pain reduction. Larger randomised controlled trials needed.

22. Patient education for neck pain. Gross et al. 2012

    Authors' Conclusions: With the exception of one trial, this review has not shown effectiveness for educational interventions.

23. Exercise therapy for treatment of non-specific low back pain. Hayden et al. 2010

Authors' Conclusions: Exercise therapy appears to be slightly effective at decreasing pain and improving function in adults with chronic low back pain, particularly in health care populations.

24. Individual patient education for low back pain. Engers et al. 2010

    Authors' Conclusions: For patients with acute or sub-acute lower back pain, intensive patient education seems to be effective. For patients with chronic lower back pain, the effectiveness of individual patient education is still unclear.

    14/24 high quality studies used.

25. Lumbar supports for prevention and treatment of lower back pain. Duijvenbode et al. 2010

    Authors' Conclusions: Moderate evidence that lumbar supports are NOT more effective than no intervention or training in preventing lower back pain.

26. Massage for lower back pain. Fulan et al. 2010

    Authors' Conclusions: Need to determine cost-effectiveness that massage might be beneficial for patients with sub-acute or chronic non-specific lower back pain.

    8/13 of studies were of high bias, the remaining 5 were of low bias.

27. Spinal manipulative therapy for chronic lower back pain. Rubenstein et al. 2011.

    Authors' Conclusions: High quality evidence suggests no clinically relevant difference between spinal manipulative therapy and other interventions for reducing pain and improving functions in patients with chronic low back pain.

    9/26 of low risk bias studies used.

    My conclusion: It's no better or worse than anything else used.

28. Spinal manipulative therapy for lower back pain. Assendelft et al. 2008

Authors' Conclusions: There is no evidence that spinal manipulative therapy is superior to other standard treatments.

Again, we are isolating HVLA as the treatment of choice.

29. Superficial heat or cold for lower backpain. French et al. 2010

Authors' Conclusions: The evidence base to support the common practice of superficial heat and cold for lower back pain is limited and there is a need for future higher quality randomised controlled trials. There is moderate evidence in a small number of trials that heat wrap therapy provides a small short-term reduction in pain and disability in a population with a mix of acute and sub-acute lower back pain, and that the addition of exercise further reduces pain and increases function. Evidence for the application of cold treatment for lower back pain is even more limited, no conclusions can be drawn here.

30. Traction for lower back pain with or without sciatica. Clarke et al. 2010

   Authors' Conclusions: <u>Implications for practice.</u> Results indicate that continuous or intermittent traction as a single treatment for lower back pain is not likely effective. <u>Implications for future research</u>: Any future research on traction for patients with lower back pain should distinguish between symptoms, pattern and duration and should be carried out according to the raised methodological standards.

31. Progressive resistance strength training for physical function in older adults. Liu et al. 2009.

   Authors' Conclusions: Evidence that progressive resistance training for improving physical function in older people including improving strength and the performance of some simple and complex activities. Some caution is needed with transferring these exercises for use with clinical populations because adverse events are not adequately reported.

32. Rehabilitation for ankle fractures in adults. Lin et al. 2008

   Authors' Conclusions: Limited evidence supporting use of a removable type of immobilisation and exercise during the immobilisation period, early commencement of weight bearing during this period, and no immobilisation after surgical fixation of ankle fracture. Limited evidence of use of manual therapy after the immobilisation period. Because of potential risk, the patient's ability to comply with the use of a removable type of immobilisation, exercise is essential. More trials required.

33. Interventions to improve adherence to exercise for chronic musculoskeletal pain (CMP) in adults. Jordan et al. 2010

Authors' Conclusions: Interventions such as supervised or individualised exercise therapy and self-manipulative techniques may enhance exercise adherence. However, high quality, randomised trials with long term follow up that explicitly address adherence to exercise and physical activity are needed.

34. Dynamic exercise programme (aerobic capacity and/or muscular strength training) in patients with rheumatoid arthritis. Hurkmans et al. 2009.

    Authors' Conclusions: Aerobic capacity training combined with muscular strength training is recommended as routine practice in patients with rheumatoid arthritis.